Ecstasy Classic Romance

"ANN," HE EXCLAIMED ANGRILY, "WE'VE GOT TO TALK."

"I don't see why, unless you want to talk about a divorce," she replied tiredly. "Anything else we had to say to each other was said years ago. We're strangers now . . . and I guess we always were."

"What do you mean by that remark?"

"We never really knew each other, David . . . we only thought we did. You might refer to it as temporary insanity . . . at least that's how it appears to me."

"Temporary," he snarled, pulling her against him.

"Let me go, David!"

"Why should I? If you don't want to talk, then we won't, but there's one form of communication we've always been good at," he whispered, lowering his lips to meet hers.

CANDLELIGHT ECSTASY CLASSIC ROMANCES

BREEZE OFF THE OCEAN,
Amii Lorin

THE CAPTIVE LOVE,
Anne N. Reisser

THE TEMPESTUOUS LOVERS,
Suzanne Simmons

SWEET EMBER,
Bonnie Drake

CANDLELIGHT ECSTASY ROMANCES®

498 PASSION'S FOLLY,
Lori Copeland

499 DARE THE DEVIL,
Elaine Raco Chase

500 TICKET TO A FANTASY,
Terri Herrington

501 INTIMATE PERSUASION,
Alice Bowen

502 CASANOVA'S
DOWNFALL,
Betty Henrichs

503 MYSTERY AT MIDNIGHT,
Eve O'Brian

QUANTITY SALES

Most Dell Books are available at special quantity discounts when purchased in bulk by corporations, organizations, and special-interest groups. Custom imprinting or excerpting can also be done to fit special needs. For details write: Dell Publishing Co., Inc., 1 Dag Hammarskjold Plaza, New York, NY 10017, Attn.: Special Sales Dept., or phone: (212) 605-3319.

INDIVIDUAL SALES

Are there any Dell Books you want but cannot find in your local stores? If so, you can order them directly from us. You can get any Dell book in print. Simply include the book's title, author, and ISBN number, if you have it, along with a check or money order (no cash can be accepted) for the full retail price plus 75¢ per copy to cover shipping and handling. Mail to: Dell Readers Service, Dept. FM, 6 Regent Street, Livingston, N.J. 07039.

OCEAN OF REGRETS

Noelle Berry McCue

A CANDLELIGHT ECSTASY CLASSIC ROMANCE

Published by
Dell Publishing Co., Inc.
1 Dag Hammarskjold Plaza
New York, New York 10017

Dell ® TM 681510, Dell Publishing Co., Inc.

A Candlelight Ecstasy Classic Romance

Candlelight Ecstasy Romance®, 1,203,540, is a registered trademark of
Dell Publishing Co., Inc.

ISBN: 0-440-16592-X

Printed in the United States of America

One Previous Edition

May 1987

10 9 8 7 6 5 4 3 2 1

WFH

To Our Readers:

By popular demand we are happy to announce that we will be bringing you two Candlelight Ecstasy Classic Romances every month.

In the upcoming months your favorite authors and their earlier best-selling Candlelight Ecstasy Romances® will be available once again.

As always, we will continue to present the distinctive sensuous love stories that you have come to expect only from Ecstasy and also the very finest work from new authors of contemporary romantic fiction.

Your suggestions and comments are always welcome. Please write to us at the address below.

Sincerely,

The Editors
Candlelight Romances
1 Dag Hammarskjold Plaza
New York, New York 10017

CHAPTER ONE

The sun filtered through thick layers of fog, as if aware of the futility of attempting to bring warmth to the cold, hostile landscape below. In swirling mockery the icy coastal wind joined forces with the damp gray mass, and together they performed their macabre dance, exciting the green and foam-flecked sea into further excesses of power and majesty, as it too dashed itself in a frenzy against the towering cliffs which cradled it.

With eyes burning from the salt spray, Anna gazed at the ferocious elements, feeling the cleansing and healing process at work deep within her. Whenever she could take the time from a very demanding career—which wasn't as often as she would have liked—she stole away to this lonely piece of San Francisco coastline and left feeling better able to cope with the demands placed upon a photographer who enjoyed a modicum of success in her own sphere.

Strangely she never attempted to photograph this particular piece of coastline, though one of her favorite pastimes was photographing the sea . . . one might almost call it her trademark, as far as her fans were concerned. But never this spot, for it would be like denuding her soul for all the world to gape at. No, she thought, a wry twist to her wide, rather sensuously full mouth. There had been too many secrets whispered into the wind in her secret place, too many tears shed with only the screeching of the gray-and-white gulls whirling and dipping overhead to see the bitterness of her rebirth. Her secret place had to be protected from all the outside world, wrapped in a cocoon of secrecy from prying eyes who would strip its secrets bare and rape the very essence of the shell she had so carefully built up around herself.

A sudden squall rose up and buffeted her bleakly shivering body, tangling in the short golden tendrils of her hair and rioting it into further curly disarray. Pulling her camel-and-black striped windcheater closer around her body, Anna forced fingers stiff from the cold to pull at the recalcitrant zipper, tugging until it was moving up from its half-closed position and nestling snugly at her throat.

With dazed eyes she looked out toward the ocean, and the horizon like a faint specter in the far distance finally brought her back from the soporific wanderings of her mind. She noticed with a start of surprise the sun beginning to give up its unequal struggle and sinking with a dull apathy beyond the horizon, sending mottled purple and crimson streaks through the fog in a last burst of energy.

Standing stiffly upright, and stamping her feet, encased in flimsy tennis shoes, to try and restore the circulation in her toes, she brushed the sand from her gray woolen slacks, her hands sliding absent-mindedly over her slim form with uncaring thoroughness.

With one last glance behind her at the beauty of the early evening sunset, Anna sighed and reluctantly turned to climb the sandy path to where her blue Triumph Spitfire was parked. Her feet slipped and slid against the damp sand, forcing her to retreat one step for every two taken forward.

Finally she reached the top of the rocky cliff, her breath coming in fitful gasps from between slightly parted lips, the salty wind, cold from the early evening fog, slicing through her lungs like shards of splintered glass.

Walking the hundred or so feet to where her car was parked, Anna was thankful to finally reach her destination, quickly turning on the ignition and pushing the heat control up full blast. At first she only felt cold air, and involuntarily she shivered, crossing her arms in front of her breast to try and encase some of her own body warmth. With a groan of thankfulness she finally felt heat emanating from below the dash, and immediately began turning the wheel preparatory to emerging from the rest-stop area of the lonely cliff road.

Anna drew a breath of relief when finally she negotiated the last twisting turn and carefully merged into the remnants of commuter traffic through town. She preferred to travel through the wharf area, or at least around it. She wasn't one for freeways except when she couldn't avoid them. She preferred more scenic routes whenever possible, and this was one of her favorites. She loved the wharf, with its tantalizing glimpses of the sea visible between quaint wooden tourist shops with their nineteenth-century flavor, and the roaming expanses of several fine restaurants. Many times she had dined here, for the seafood was freshly caught and excellently prepared, and she always loved looking through wide plate-glass windows at the water seemingly just below.

The endless smell of fish became particularly strong as she negotiated the open-air fish market for which the wharf was so famous, her car window half down. Like a fool she had overcompensated for the cold . . . and now was uncomfortably warm. The delicious aromas teasing her nostrils were causing unpleasant sensations in her stomach, reminding her that her last meal had been a long time ago and eaten on the run. In fact, she thought with a wry twist of her lips, she had only managed to choke down about half of a dry and very unappetizing sandwich between photographic assignments. Eating in a car while speeding down the Bayshore Freeway, with only minutes between shots, which just happen to be across town from each other, doesn't make for particularly good digestion.

As her stomach began growling in earnest, so did Anna's temper shorten. "Why in the world didn't I take the other way around and avoid all these people," she mumbled, the sound of her own voice blending with the many languages she could hear around her from the tourists flocking the raised wooden sidewalks.

At last she was turning her car into the underground parking area of the rather imposing apartment complex she called home, and she expelled her breath in a sigh of relief. Negotiating the ramp, she drove the short distance to her stall, checking that the doors were securely locked before walking toward the disreputable-looking elevator, with its pornographic messages scrawled across the gray surface of the door.

Reaching the fifteenth floor, Anna gave a start of surprise as the elevator jerked to a stop, opening its cumbersome bulk with a groan of protest. Her mind had been a thousand miles away, and as she stepped out onto plushly carpeted hallway surfaces, she once again ran a tired hand over the back of her neck. Quick footsteps were muffled as she negotiated the long hall, at the same time rummaging in her bag.

"Damn," she muttered, feeling more frustrated than she should at the elusiveness of her keys, grabbing the offending objects which as usual had slipped to the bottom of her purse.

Anna's soft-soled shoes made little sound on the tile entry hall, but she glanced down in satisfaction at the shine

10

on the gold-and-brown-swirled surface, remembering belatedly that today was one of the housekeeper's regular days. She paid dearly for Mrs. Harrison's services twice a week, but she was a jewel at any price, she thought with a smile.

Glancing around at the immaculate appearance of her black-and-gold-toned living room, Anna felt a rush of thankfulness for the material things of life which, through a job she loved, she had been able to provide for herself. Life was satisfying, and her work made up a great proportion of that life, she thought a trifle smugly.

Walking toward her bedroom, she skirted the formal dining room and once again entered the hall. Forcing her steps to quicken after taking a longing glance at the bed, she walked through the beauty of silver-and-gold spread and matching drapes, fighting down the urge to lie down and pretend she wasn't home when Carl came to pick her up for their dinner date.

With the welcome steam from the bath penetrating her tired muscles, Anna felt awful for the thoughts which had been running through her mind just moments before. After all, she scolded herself mentally, Carl was one of the best friends she had, and she should appreciate him more. Oh, at times he came on too strong, trying to order her life when, to her, it was as well ordered as she wanted it to be. She was her own woman, and to become that way had meant a long, painful, and sometimes frightening uphill struggle . . . but she'd achieved it, and no man was going to take it away from her . . . not ever again!

Anna released the plug in the tub and, standing, turned on the shower full blast. The cold stinging needles which sprayed her skin caused her to gasp, but dispelled successfully the direction her thoughts were taking. Sometimes memory flooded back, but for her sanity she had learned well all the tricks to keeping her thoughts under control. Now when she remembered the naive and loving girl she

11

had been five years ago, she shuddered at her own trusting stupidity and channelled her mind away from the image of herself as she was then. Instead she forced herself to feel pity and disgust for that girl . . . and only admiration for what she had been able to make of her life in spite of what had happened.

Stepping out of the bathtub, she quickly towelled her body. She slipped on her underclothes, their silken surfaces cool against her skin. Smoothing over her legs nylons which were only slightly darker than the honey tan she had managed to acquire despite the frantic working schedule of the summer months, Anna sat down at her dressing table. Shading blue eye shadow over her lids to accentuate the violet blue of her eyes, she was glad her lashes were long and naturally curling. All they needed was a touch of sable brown mascara and she was set. She wore very little makeup usually, but right now her face was showing definite signs of fatigue, and she decided to use a little blusher over her high cheekbones.

Finally satisfied with her appearance, she ran a quick comb through the slightly damp and curling tendrils of her hair, the light showing reddish highlights nestling among the blond. Thank goodness for wash and wear haircuts, she thought, jumping up and going to grab her dress from the closet. If the clock beside the bed was right, Carl would be ringing the bell any moment, and he hated it when she wasn't ready when he arrived. Smoothing the royal blue shantung sheath down over her hips, Anna turned for one last look at her reflection. This dress was one of her favorites, molding her figure as if made for her. Sleeveless, with a short mandarin collar, it was definitely of Chinese design, right down to the midthigh slit in the hem.

"Damn," she muttered, searching frantically for her blue sling-backed pumps as she heard the ringing of the doorbell. Finding them in the back of her closet, she clutched them in her hand and ran across the room to grab a handkerchief from her drawer, stuffing it haphazardly into her evening bag.

"I'm coming," she called, trying to walk and slip the second shoe on while still in motion, an impossible feat, as she soon discovered. With one hand releasing the door latch, the other one finally managed the shoe, and taking a deep and calming breath, she quietly and composedly opened the door.

"Anna, lovely and cool as always," Carl murmured, kissing the cheek turned to him and walking past her into the living room.

"Thank you, Carl," Anna said, hoping he couldn't hear the irony in her voice. Following him into the living room she asked, "Would you like a drink?"

"Yes, I believe I would," he affirmed, pulling up knife-creased trousers before sitting back on the couch.

"Scotch?" Anna questioned with a lift of her brow.

"That'll be fine."

Crossing to the small but beautifully appointed bar in the corner, Anna felt a vague irritation. Why in the world did she bother asking when she knew very well Carl never drank anything but Scotch, and only the best of that. She couldn't tell one from another, but Carl insisted there was a difference. Well, maybe if she herself liked Scotch, or even tolerated it, she thought wryly, she might notice a difference, too.

After fetching ice from the refrigerator in the kitchen, another task that caused that dissatisfied bubble of irritation to burst inside of her, she returned to pour the alcohol over the tinkling ice cubes, her mouth pursing in anger when she turned to face Carl and saw him apparently at home and immersed in her newspaper. Really, Carl was the absolute limit sometimes, she thought, a frown stealing across her forehead, and a renewal of her earlier headache beginning to make itself felt. He had been out of town for

13

the last couple of weeks, and now he just sat here as detached and unaware of her as if he'd seen her yesterday.

Handing Carl his drink, she returned to the kitchen and poured herself an orange juice, adding a generous measure of ice to her own glass. For a moment she stood there, not really seeing the pristine coolness of white walls and copper-toned fitments.

What in the world was wrong with her tonight; she wasn't normally this bitchy. Being tired was one thing, but this was something else again. Tiredness couldn't account for the fact that her body felt as taut and strung out as a high tension wire, couldn't explain away the ache low in the pit of her stomach. No . . . if she were honest with herself, she knew her earlier foray into the past was responsible. The sensuality she was normally able to keep under control had awakened with a vengeance at those thoughts, and she felt almost physically sick at the moment.

A memory of hard brown hands caressing her heated skin into unbearable pleasure, and of a firm, sensuous mouth driving her wild with desire, exploded in her mind. God, she thought, closing her eyes in agony. She had loved him so much . . . and at times during their marriage had felt violent, as if she would claw herself right into his skin until his tall, muscular body absorbed her completely.

Dear God! What am I doing? With a groan of disgust she took a shaky breath, taking a nervous swallow of the cool liquid in her glass and walking to the cabinet where she kept her aspirin. Taking two in her mouth, she finished the rest of her drink, and on legs which felt like rubber returned the orange juice to the refrigerator.

Anna fought for control, burying her face in the cloth she withdrew hurriedly from the towel cabinet. None of this was Carl's fault, she thought wretchedly. Specters from the past were responsible, sending shades of memory to haunt her present. Well, she just wouldn't let them . . .

she couldn't! Carl was a friend, though, if she were honest with herself, he would like to be a lot more. Several times she had talked like mad to prevent the proposal she'd sensed was coming, and obviously he had gotten the message. She couldn't feel that way toward him, though God alone knew why. Maybe she had become frigid over the years! With a sob of despair she couldn't help thinking that Carl had every reason to believe that of her.

If the traumatic experiences she had suffered through in the past had caused her to be frigid . . . then so be it. Never would she want to be in the vulnerable position she'd placed herself in before. She was older and a lot wiser now and wouldn't want to risk anyone having that much power over her.

When he had walked out on her without a word of explanation, disappearing from her life as if he'd never existed, except for the remembrance he had left behind so callously, she had wanted to die. Finally, after long illness and months of dark despair, she had remade her life around her work, finding the fulfillment in taking beautiful pictures filling the void.

She had been lucky, selling more and more of her work to various magazines, slowly and painstakingly building a name for herself . . . until she was now in the enviable position of being in demand by many on a free-lance basis. With her own studio and two good friends and valuable employees to help her cope with the enlarging and developing, not to mention the paperwork involved in the inventory and bookkeeping, her future was secure . . . and it would stay that way, she vowed silently. She would stick with Carl, stodgy but sweet, and very good to her. He was safe . . . as was the life she had built up around herself, and she never wanted to be awakened again, not sexually, emotionally, or any other way!

Finally gaining some composure by the very harshness of her thoughts, Anna walked out of the kitchen and through the dining room. Carl was just where she'd left him, still immersed in the paper, his drink finished and re-placed upon the bar in his usual fastidious fashion. She doubted if he had even noticed her absence, and with a shaky breath catching in her throat she was suddenly immensely grateful for that fact.

"Ready, darling?" Carl questioned, folding the paper meticulously and rising to his feet.

"Yes," she replied, walking toward the hall closet and turning out the lights as she went. "I just have to get my wrap."

In the softly subdued luxury of Carl's silver-gray Continental, rich with pale blue leather upholstery and wood dashboard paneling, she found her mind once again wandering back to the images conjured up from the past and almost moaned aloud. With perspiration beginning to bead her forehead she turned to Carl.

"Could you turn the heat down a little?"

"Of course," he replied, glancing toward her with a puzzled look. "Aren't you feeling well, darling? You're usually asking me to turn the heater up, not the other way around."

"No . . . I'm all right, Carl," she snapped. "Is it a crime to feel warm once in a while?"

Anna glanced over at Carl's set face, feeling like every kind of a heel for snapping at him like that. It was almost as if she were trying to pick an argument, anything to keep her mind off the introspection of her own tortured thoughts. With a sigh she quietly apologized, closing her eyes against the pain drumming against her temples with renewed force.

"Anna . . . this isn't like you," Carl stated, turning away from his intent survey of the steady stream of city traffic to frown at the whiteness of her face. "Is there something wrong? Something I could help you with?"

"No . . . I've just got a headache . . . nothing to worry

16

about, Carl. I don't know why I'm being such a beast to you. Why do you bother with me anyway?"

"I think you know the answer to that as well as I do," he said, his voice quiet.

Glancing at Carl's absorbed face as he negotiated one of San Francisco's famous hill streets, which seemed almost perpendicular as the car climbed toward the summit, Anna put out her hand, patting Carl's sleeve, feeling the fine worsted material of his beige suit warm against her fingers.

"I'm sorry, Carl," she whispered. "You're so good to me, such a good friend. I . . . I just don't . . ."

"I know, Anna," he interrupted, raising one hand from the wheel to pat her hand comfortingly. "Believe me, I understand you don't return my feelings . . . and maybe you're right," he stated firmly, causing Anna to glance at him in surprise.

With the quiet laugh which seemed surprising in such a large man, but which somehow suited his restrained personality so well, Carl explained.

"I've done a lot of thinking about our relationship while I've been away, Anna. I was all set to ask you to marry me the last time we were together . . . you knew that, didn't you?"

At her affirmative nod he smiled ruefully. "I guessed from your avoidance of the subject that you had."

"Oh, Carl," she choked, feeling like a criminal for causing the least hurt to this understanding man who was so much a friend to her.

"Now, now . . . none of that, darling," he scolded good-naturedly. "Let me finish before you start feeling guilty, hum?"

"All right," she sniffed. "But before you do can I blow my nose?"

When their laughter had finally died down, Carl finished his earlier conversation.

"Number one, Anna . . . I'm too old for you," he stated firmly and motioned her to silence when she began to protest. "No . . . you know it's true. Oh, I know that many people marry and have wonderful relationships with a gap of twenty years between them, but it's not really a matter of years, is it?" At her puzzled frown he went on to explain himself more fully. "As much as I hate to admit it, I've become rather set in my ways. Nearing fifty, slightly balding, and a little too broad in the middle to be a good match for a young woman like yourself."

"Oh, Carl . . . you're a darling, and any woman would be proud to be your wife. It's not your fault that I . . . that I . . ."

Smiling, he blurted: "That I don't turn you on?"

Shocked at his candidness, Anna turned startled blue eyes in his direction and sighed with relief when she noted his slightly red face and twinkling brown eyes. *Poor Carl,* she thought as she smiled at him, *he shocked himself with that one!*

"Anyway, Anna . . . I decided at first that my heart was broken, but then realized it was no more than my masculine pride rearing its ugly head. I came to the surprising conclusion, my dear, that like you, I enjoy our relationship the way it is."

"I'm glad, Carl," she sighed. "I wouldn't want to lose you. I know that sounds selfish, considering I don't give you back nearly as much as you give me in warmth and a good shoulder to cry on . . . but you're the dearest friend I have."

Patting her hand once again, he sat up straighter, shrugging his shoulders, which had been held stiffly with tension, and once again smiling in her direction. "I'm glad . . . for both our friendship and the fact that this conversation's over with," he stated outrageously, making her laugh in affection and genuine amusement . . . and for the rest of the evening Anna was determined that she would do ev-

18

erything in her power to make it a specially delightful one for him.

Driving through the financial district of San Francisco, they ended their journey on Clay Street, just across from the Transamerica Pyramid building. Handing the keys to the parking attendant, Carl took her arm and led her across the street to the entrance of Don Nunzio's restaurant. As they walked she glanced over her shoulder, admiring the clean, classic lines of the pyramid-shaped structure which seemed to disappear upward, its pointed tip invisible in the fog.

Entering, she was pleased that Carl had reserved their usual table. All at once the very familiarity of doing the expected was no longer irritating to her, but somehow comforting.

The baked turbot was delicious, the flavor enhanced by a superlative white wine. While eating, she and Carl talked as they never had before. It was as if bringing their relationship out in the open as they had was the forerunner to a new and closer understanding. In those moments of shared companionship she realized for the first time how lost she would be without Carl. *Never again,* she vowed silently, watching him while he explained some business deal he was presently conducting. Never again would she be irritated by Carl's staid and sometimes overly cautious attitudes, for these were the very qualities which had drawn her to him in the first place. If she hadn't considered Carl 'safe,' she knew she would have missed out on a wonderful relationship, a relationship which she had foolishly taken for granted.

Later that evening while they sat in her apartment she let her thoughts wander. The ringing of the telephone interrupted the pleasant mind wandering she was indulging in, and with a sigh she got up and went into her bedroom so she wouldn't interfere with Carl's eleven o'clock news

19

watching. Lifting the receiver, Anna was surprised to hear Carla's voice on the other end.

"Anna, is that you?"

"Hi, Carla," she replied. "You sound upset, is anything wrong?"

"I'm not upset, stupid . . . just excited," Carla rejoined with a laugh. "I don't know why you always have to assume the worst, Anna."

"Well, I'm just superstitious, I guess. Anyway, what's up?"

"Just the most wonderful thing that could happen just now . . . that's all," Carla said, her voice becoming squeaky with excitement.

"Carla, if you don't tell me what's happened this minute," Anna threatened, "I'll wring your neck when I get in tomorrow."

"Now, now . . . there's no need to get hostile," she replied, a gurgle of laughter bubbling up in her throat.

Anna couldn't imagine what had gotten Carla into this state of tense excitement, but she knew it had to be something pretty great. Carla was an attractive woman in her early forties, divorced, with two children to support. Because of the responsibilities thrust upon her when the children were quite small, Anna knew that Carla was usually very serious-minded and not one to jump into something without looking it over carefully first.

Carla had come to handle the secretarial side of the studio three years ago, doing a wonderful job of it, too. Anna had began to depend more and more upon Carla's opinions and suggestions, finding that most of the time they worked out quite well. Also, Anna knew that whether she deserved it or not, Carla considered her a good friend. Mainly, Anna suspected, because she understood and sympathized with the hardships Carla faced in raising two children virtually alone, never objecting when she had to leave early to take them to the doctor or on the infrequent occasions when she had to stay at home to nurse them.

"All right, you win," Carla continued, once again drawing Anna's attention to the conversation. "Do you remember that organization we send money to support every year?"

"We send money to several charities," Anna replied, puzzled at the trend their conversation was taking. What in the world, she thought, was so exciting about giving money away?

"No . . . I'm talking about the organization on saving the whales . . . I'm so excited I can't think of what they call themselves. Just a minute, I wrote it down somewhere."

"It's okay, Carla . . . I know who you're talking about, don't worry."

"Oh, good" Carla breathed. "Anyway, they called yesterday. Or rather one of their representatives came by to talk to you about taking some photographs for them."

"But they have their own people for assignments like that, Carla," she puzzled. "Why would they want to hire a free-lancer?"

"Well, according to Mr. Curtis," Carla began. "It seems they're beginning a nationwide publicity campaign to get the support of the people against the yearly slaughter of the whales. They saw some of your work last month at that gallery in the city, and it seems they were terribly impressed with your pictures taken just off Seal Rock," Carla explained, her voice once again rising excitedly. "You know the series of photos I mean?"

"Yes," Anna replied. "But I still don't understand what all the excitement is about."

"You will if you'll just give me a chance to get on with it!"

"Okay," Anna laughed. "Fire away."

"Well, this Mr. Curtis explained their need for a professional photographer of your standard to cover the convention they're planning as a sort of kickoff to their campaign. Really, Anna, it just couldn't have come at a better time."

"Why?"

"Because the convention starts next week . . . and we were just discussing Friday how slow the next couple of weeks looked. Right?"

"You can say that again," Anna replied with a sigh. "Things haven't been this slow for a long time. Except for Allan having a couple of weddings to cover, it looked as if both of us would get that vacation we've been promising ourselves for the best part of six months. Why in the world would you want me to take this assignment and foul our plans up, Carla? Money's not quite everything, you know. At least, I hope you do."

"No . . . but it sure helps," Carla retorted. "Anyway, it's not money we're talking about, Anna. Don't you know what this could mean to your career, you nut?"

"I know, I know . . . but I need a break, Carla . . . both of us do. You haven't had a vacation in over a year and a half, and I don't remember the last time I took a real vacation."

"But it'll only be for a week or so, Anna."

"No, Carla! Chances are we'll get back and find we're snowed under," Anna exclaimed. "Just like the last time, remember?"

"All right, be stubborn. This could be the chance of a lifetime, and if you think we're not going to discuss it further, Anna . . . then you've got another think coming."

Anna sighed. "Okay, Carla. We'll discuss it in the morning when you can give me all the facts, but don't think you're going to change my mind. They'll just have to find somebody else."

"Fine, love," Carla chirped. "See you tomorrow."

After bidding Carl goodnight Anna settled down in the

comfort of her bed with a groan of relief. Yawning, she checked the setting on the alarm before turning off the light. As she lay in the comforting darkness, her mind went over her conversation with Carla for the hundredth time, the thoughts revolving around and around in her head, causing her to toss and turn in active discomfort. Really, she thought with exasperation. If she didn't stop this and get to sleep, she wouldn't be fit for work tomorrow, and she had some enlargements she wanted to work on, as well as developing that roll and readying them for the portfolio she had to turn in for the magazine series she was working on.

Why did Carla have to call tonight, she thought irrationally. She had been physically and mentally relaxed for a change, and now her mind was working overtime. No, she just wouldn't do it, no matter what they offered. Sometimes a limit has to be set, and as far as she was concerned, she'd already crossed the line weeks ago. With this conclusion reached, Anna felt sleep overtaking her. With one last snuggle of her head in the whiteness of the pillowcase she felt her thoughts drifting away, her body relaxing even more pleasurably.

The next morning found Anna a little less complacent as she parked her car in the lot, walking the short block to the studio. The more she thought about the conversation with Carla, the more she mistrusted that elated note of confidence in her voice when she rang off. Knowing Carla, there was more to this than she told her over the phone. I just hope I can withstand the bait, Anna thought in amusement. Sometimes it was difficult remembering she was the boss. When Carla got a bee in her bonnet, there was no peace until she got her own way, as both she and Al had good reason to know. The fact that Carla's hunches about the advisibility of taking certain steps nearly always paid off was what was so maddening! Well, whether or not Carla had a winning hunch, she had a feeling this was going to be one of her more fierce battles, and Anna shook her head in resignation as she opened the door and entered the studio.

CHAPTER TWO

Anna's supposition proved more accurate than even she had foreseen. As soon as she entered the white-walled, airy studio after passing Carla's empty desk in the vestibule, she was immediately beseiged by Carla and Al, both talking at once.

"Hey honey, this is great news!" Al cried, hugging Anna exuberantly before she had taken more than two steps into the room. With a strained smile Anna disengaged herself from Al's eager embrace with difficulty. His huge bulk shook with laughter, the red-and-green checked shirt he wore making him look even more like Santa Claus than ever, she thought fondly. Maybe that was why he was an expert at photographing children . . . not to mention some naive adults, she thought, turning and sending a baleful glance at Carla.

"Now . . . there's no reason to be mad, Anna," Carla cajoled, perching herself upon the end of a long table which leaned precariously against the far wall.

"Why is it being taken for granted I'm going to take this assignment, you two? You know I have no intention . . ."

25

"But Anna," Carla interrupted. "Don't you even want to know where the convention's being held?"

At the innocent enquiry Anna braced herself. Here goes, she thought. Now for the ace up Carla's sleeve.

"Where is it being held then, for goodness sake?"

"Long Beach, that's where," Carla crowed triumphantly.

"Long Beach?" Anna breathed, her eyes beginning to reflect Carla's excitement.

"Yes," Carla replied, unnecessarily smoothing her dark hair, which was confined in a tight twist on the top of her head. The severe style complemented Carla's high cheekbones, while at the same time drawing attention to her slender neck and the softness of her oval face. "It's to be held aboard the *Queen Mary*."

"The *Queen Mary*?"

"Yep," Al responded, winking at Carla as he settled his large frame gingerly upon a rather rickety chair. Turning to face Anna, he laughed. "Now what do you say, honey?"

With an image in her mind of long stretches of white sand leading to glorious expanses of green and foam-flecked ocean, Anna breathed: "What do you think?"

"I knew it!" Carla yelled, jumping down and nearly knocking Anna off her feet. "You don't have to worry about anything, honey. Just go and enjoy yourself . . . Al and I can manage fine."

"No!"

"What do you mean . . . no?"

"I'll only go on one condition. You have to come with me, Carla."

"But Anna, who'll handle all the calls and appointments, not to mention . . ."

"What do you think I am, Carla?" Al's booming voice rang out, causing both Anna and Carla to jump in surprise. "We'll use the phone message unit for when I have to be out on an assignment. The rest of the problems can be put off for a week, can't they?"

"Well . . . I guess so, but . . ."

"If you're worried about the kids," Anna began determinedly, "you know your mother will come and stay. Anyway, Gary's sixteen and quite capable of taking care of his sister with your mother there to supervise."

"I know that. Gary and Susan are both good kids, but I hate the thought of leaving them for a week."

"You need a break yourself, Carla," Anna cajoled. "You can make it up to them when we get back. Maybe rent a place at the beach for a couple of weeks."

"But you'll need me more here, Anna."

"Not as much as I'll need you in Long Beach," Anna smiled. "So . . . it's settled?"

"You can bet on it," rumbled Al, getting up slowly and rubbing his hands together in satisfaction. "It's going to be great around this place without any blathering females for a whole week."

By the time Friday approached, Anna didn't know if she was on her head or her heels. If it hadn't been for Carla, once again her usual calmly efficient self, Anna didn't know what she would have done. All the arrangements had been finalized with Mr. Curtis, and she and Carla had her car loaded down with luggage. They planned leaving as early as possible this afternoon, hoping to avoid as much commuter traffic as possible. Mr. Curtis had suggested calling midway for reservations for the night, just in case the valley fog became too dangerous for driving. Anna and Carla thought it was a good idea. It would give them time to relax, and they weren't due to take over their rooms on the *Queen Mary* until after twelve o'clock on Saturday anyway.

While Carla made a last-minute phone call to her mother, Al helped Anna carefully load her equipment into the back seat of her already overloaded Triumph. Thank God for car racks, she thought, blowing a stray wisp of hair off her forehead. They would have never managed to cram all this stuff inside the car.

"Well, that's everything," Al puffed in satisfaction.

Carla, her phone call evidently satisfactory if the smile on her face was anything to go by, also said her good-byes to Al, settling herself in the passenger seat with a sigh of relief.

With a last wave of good-bye they set off, and Anna turned to Carla with a grin.

"I began to think we weren't going to make it!"

"With Al behind us pushing and shoving, did you have any doubts?" Carla laughed.

They had been driving for about two hours when Anna noticed the large windmill off to the left.

"Carla, there's Split Pea Andersen's restaurant. Want to stop and eat since we missed lunch? I don't know about you, but my stomach thinks I've forgotten how to chew!"

"Perfect, I'm starving!"

After wandering around and looking at all the adjoining shop had to offer, which was considerable in light of the fact that they did a booming tourist trade, Anna and Carla were finally seated in the restaurant. After giving their orders to a perky young waitress, Carla turned to Anna.

"I admit I'm as excited as a kid about this trip."

"Hmmm," Anna mumbled, swallowing the cracker she'd stuffed in her mouth. "Me too!"

"Mr. Curtis was telling me that the guy who heads this organization is going to be one of the principal speakers."

"What's his name?"

"David Carruthers," Carla replied, spooning sugar into her coffee. "No, that's not right . . . it's David Carmichael."

At her words Anna's hands clenched, her face whitening. Taking a deep breath, she tried to control the hysteria she felt rising up inside. Dear God . . . it couldn't be! "What did you say his name is?" she whispered.

28

"David Carmichael," Carla repeated. "From what Mr. Curtis told me, he sounds a rather interesting character. Seems he has pots of money from hotel chains spread up and down the coast, but the unusual part is he's also a renowned oceanographer. From the impression I got, it seems the sea is his first love."

Anna sipped her coffee with shaking hands, glad for the diversion created by the waitress when she returned at that moment with their meals. Thank God Carla hadn't noticed anything out of the ordinary, she thought, making a supreme effort to gain control of herself.

They had to go back, she thought frantically. She just couldn't go ahead with this assignment . . . not if it meant David was going to be there. God in Heaven, why hadn't she checked before committing herself? It was too late now; she would have to show up if her career meant anything to her, and God knows it was all she had left after David. . . .

No! She wouldn't think of the past, that was dead and buried. She probably wouldn't even come close to him. There would be hundreds of people there, and maybe it would be possible to get lost in the crowd, she comforted herself, while knowing deep down inside how unlikely that would be. Fighting sudden tears, Carla's words came back to her. "It seems the sea is his first love."

"His only love," Anna whispered.

"Is it morning, already?" Carla mumbled, sitting up in bed and running her hands over her face, still fogged from sleep.

"It's only seven o'clock . . . go back to sleep if you want."

Carla settled back onto the pillow with a sigh, but as she observed Anna, who remained standing by the window, something about the tense quality of her back disturbed her.

"Anna, is something the matter? Why aren't you asleep?"

"Don't be silly, Carla. What could be wrong at this hour of the morning? I guess I'm just nervous about setting off in all this fog," Anna shuddered, crossing her arms around her body and gripping her elbows. She remained with her back turned toward Carla, afraid her friend would see the haunted expression in her eyes.

"Look, Anna," Carla reassured, tucking the covers more securely around her chin. "I'm sure by the time we've had breakfast and loaded the car, the fog will have burned off. Anyway, it couldn't be as bad during the day as it was last night."

"I know . . . I'm just being silly, anticipating the worst," Anna agreed.

Last evening had been something of a nightmare for the both of them, Anna remembered. The swirling valley fog had become denser and more treacherous as evening approached, until both she and Carla had been silent in nervous reaction.

The creeping gray mass had lowered and become a ground fog, obliterating the highway's white dividing lines almost entirely.

Before the conditions had worsened, she had taken several exits along the way, trying to find accomodation for the night, but all the motels along Interstate 5 had been full. It was only to be expected, of course, that others would have the same idea, but it hadn't made their predicament any less dangerous.

Mr. Curtis had suggested making reservations midway just as a precaution . . . but both she and Carla had completely forgotten to take his advice. When Carla remembered before leaving, like a fool she had told her not to bother, there were bound to be plenty of vacancies, since it was winter and not the height of the tourist season. How wrong could one person be? By the time she had realized her mistake, it was much too late for regrets.

Lost in thought, Anna hadn't noticed a lightening in the density outside the motel window. With a sigh of relief she noticed the fog did seem to be lifting slightly, for now she was able to see the outline of the central courtyard and the massive parking area to her left. Though still thick, the fog had risen several feet from ground level, so maybe Carla was right and it would be safe for driving in another couple of hours.

Anna glanced back at the again-sleeping Carla lying still and relaxed, and felt a momentary twinge of envy flow through her when her gaze encompassed the rumpled covers of her own matching twin. There had been little sleep for her during the night. Her body seemed to have a life of its own, jerking her awake when she did finally manage to fall asleep. After what had seemed hours of struggle she had finally given in, pacing the floor in the darkness.

Turning, Anna quietly gathered her clothes and took them into the dressing area of their small motel room. Like all motels it had an impersonal air, emphasized by the white, uniform towels lying precisely over the chrome towel racks and the individually wrapped, miniature bars of soap lying beside the basins.

Turning on the water in the small bathtub, Anna adjusted the flow, shedding her gown and stepping inside. Her body tingled pleasurably as she scrubbed her flesh, her aching muscles soothed by the warmth. She had forgotten to get her shampoo out of her overnight case, but for once the bar soap would have to serve the purpose.

After rinsing her hair Anna turned off the faucet, stepping out onto the cold tile floor and drying herself on the rather rough towels the motel provided. Bending to release the filmy water, she then straightened, wrapping her hair in a dry towel. She cringed from her reflection in the mir-

31

ror, fogged with moisture, which covered the wall above the basin area.

Dear God, if she tried not to think . . . to shut her mind to everything but the mundane, mechanical motions one does every day . . . there was always something to bring her torment into focus. Putting her hands upward to cover her cheeks, she felt the moisture from her tears. Covering her face completely, she let the tears flow, her shoulders shaking in silent sobs.

After the tumult of her emotions had spent themselves, Anna felt somewhat better. Bathing her reddened eyes, she dried her face, donning casual slacks and an open-throated shirtwaister of teal blue. She knew the color complemented the blue of her eyes and her blond coloring . . . hadn't David told her so . . . so very many times?

"Anna, you through in there? I want to shower and go get some breakfast," Carla called, turning the door handle. "I'm starving."

"You're always starving," Anna laughed, unlocking the door and stepping past Carla. "How you manage to stay so slim when you eat like a horse is beyond me!"

"Huh! You should talk," Carla laughed, shivering as she hurried past Anna. "Ugh . . . it's freezing in here. Be a love and turn up the thermostat, will you? I can't figure out how to work the darned thing."

Funnily enough, Anna hadn't been conscious of the cold room until Carla mentioned it. It's strange what your emotions were capable of blocking out of your consciousness, she thought, fiddling with the thermostat dial. The reassuring sound of the heater coming on filled the room, blending with the noise of the water. No wonder Carla woke up, Anna thought, smiling to herself as she repacked all but her makeup.

This she carried to the dressing table, putting it on absent-mindedly while letting her memories flow. It had never been any good, trying to shut David out of her mind, she knew that now. The hurt of the past had affected her present, and if she didn't face herself with the truth, it would mar any future she made for herself.

Closing her eyes, Anna leaned her elbows upon the marble-topped surface of the dressing table. Suddenly it was summer again, and she could smell the sea and hear the pounding surf beckoning her through the window of the small cottage she'd rented for the week. . . .

Jumping up from the studio couch which served as her bed, Anna donned a lemon-yellow bikini hurriedly, brushing her long blond hair back from her face and tying it back in a ponytail. Her feet flew over the warm sand, skirting small rocks and shells skillfully. She'd waited so long for this vacation, she thought, gasping as her body hit the coolness of pounding waves. As she swam, the early morning sun felt soothingly warm on the top of her head. Turning her body with the skill of an expert swimmer, she floated upon her back, feeling the skin of her neck and throat absorbing the heat, enjoying the feeling of being a part of the sea and sky. The waves lifted her body gently, the blue-green surface dancing with sparkling pinnacles of light where the sun shimmered hotly upon its surface.

After playing about in the water, Anna felt her legs tiring and knew it was time to swim toward shore. Turning, she noticed with alarm how far the waves had carried her. With a feeling of panic, legs suddenly leaden, she began a slow crawl, but no matter how hard she swam, she didn't seem to be getting any closer to shore. By now she was gasping for air, her lungs at bursting point from her efforts. Turning onto her back once again, she tried to rest, but the once-friendly waves were fighting her now, spewing their salty tentacles around her nose and mouth and causing her to choke and throw her body forward. She tread water, but she knew with a feeling of terror that her legs wouldn't hold her up much longer.

Despair gripped her as she wondered if these were her

last moments. *Dear God, help me!* Though her cry was silent, she felt as if she screamed it at the top of her lungs . . . and like an answer to her prayer she saw a cabin cruiser in the distance. She tried frantically to call for help, waving her arms wildly above her head, but all she succeeded in doing was to swallow more sea water. She was going down . . . down into a cool green nothingness, and by now her limbs were so heavy, so very heavy, it hardly seemed worth the effort to try and pull herself out of the cradle of the sea. Without conscious thought her head once more surfaced, and for a moment she saw the sleek white lines of the cabin cruiser close . . . so very close. There was a man on the deck and he appeared to be throwing something. *Funny,* she thought, swallowing more water as she chuckled out loud. Here she was drowning and someone was throwing things at her!

There was a shout, or maybe it was the roaring in her ears as she once again slipped below the surface. Now the water was no longer cold . . . no longer the enemy. There was softness, and gentleness. She hadn't felt so comforted since her mother died, she thought in amazement. Dying's so pleasant, she thought with wonder . . . not at all as she'd imagined it to be. Her body was floating downward . . . no, she was flying . . . soaring through green sky . . . so very dark a green it was almost black. She felt something on her arms trying to keep her from flying away into the darkness, and she struggled against the force, but there was no longer any strength to ward off the intrusion . . . her arms wouldn't obey her commands. *It doesn't matter,* she thought, no longer fighting the force. The darkness was all around her now, and the sea was tugging playfully at her hair.

Anna heard the sound of someone retching violently. *Poor thing,* she thought, *they sound like they're terribly sick.* Suddenly she was conscious of lying on a hard, cold surface, and there was a terrible weight upon her body.

The weight was unbearable, pummelling her back with savage pushing motions and pressing her breasts painfully against a hard wooden surface. She began to struggle against the pressure, writhing her body away from her tormentor . . . and as she moved she heard a rasping voice cursing above her and knew it was a man's hands which were causing all the discomfort.

"Damn it, lie still!"

"Get off of me," she cried, her voice sounding like a whisper even to her own ears. Now she knew who it was she'd heard being sick, and as hard hands turned her swiftly over and strong sinewy arms cradled her now trembling body next to his warmth, Anna closed her eyes in embarrassment.

"Hey, honey. Don't flake out on me again," his voice demanded, but she found she couldn't open her eyes . . . she was too tired . . . just too tired to do more than moan. Once again her breath seemed to be suspended, and she felt a clutching pain in her chest. The darkness was coming close again, and her heavy eyelids flew open in terror . . . to stare into the greenest eyes she'd ever seen. At that moment those eyes seemed to be willing her to do his bidding, and with a sense of fatality gripping her she saw his head lower . . . until his thick black lashes covered them . . . as the blackness had covered the green of the sea. Then his mouth was on hers, opening her lips with gentle fingers, and his breath was sweet . . . so very sweet filling her mouth. His lips were cool and salty like the sea, yet hard and comforting. With a moan of protest she felt his mouth lift from hers . . . and her last thought before sinking into darkness was that it wasn't like before. Now she could hear her own heartbeat, her own breath falling from her lips like a sigh, and a hard, muscular warmth keeping her from flying away.

Anna snuggled deeper into the softness of the bed, lifting the warm thickness of the blankets more firmly around her. She was so comfortable, and she luxuriated in the feeling of security the blankets gave her. A gentle rocking motion was lulling her back to sleep, and she covered her mouth with her hand as she muffled a huge yawn.

"So . . . you're awake at last!"

At the sound of the deep male voice Anna's eyes flew open in alarm, and she sat up quickly, the blankets falling around her waist. A fiery blush suffused her face as with a strangled gasp she jerked the blankets up to her chin, belatedly trying to cover her nakedness from devilish green eyes which seemed to burn over her soft flesh unreservedly.

"Where . . . where am I?"

"You're aboard my boat," he replied softly, handing her a mug of hot liquid, which Anna made no attempt to grasp.

"It's just coffee, honey. Come on, take it."

"No thank you," Anna replied primly, once more feeling her face becoming uncomfortably hot.

"Ah, I see your predicament," he chuckled, his eyes roaming to the rounded shape of her breasts outlined clearly by the blanket. "Don't upset yourself unnecessarily, honey. I've seen it all before, you know."

"You mean you . . . you," Anna spluttered, her face now crimson with anger. "You have a lot of nerve, Mr. . . . ?"

"Carmichael, but you can call me David, honey."

"Well, I have no intention of calling you David, and you have no business calling me honey!"

"Since I don't happen to know your name, honey . . . what else am I going to call you? There wasn't time for a formal introduction when I pulled you out of the water."

Suddenly full memory flooded through Anna's mind, and she bit her lower lip as thoughts of her earlier terror smote her, her eyes once again clouding in fear.

With a hurried movement David put the coffee down on a ledge bolted to the wall, which Anna supposed must serve as a dining table. In two strides he was beside her, sitting close to her on what she now realized was a wide bunk, also fitted securely to the wall of the boat.

Warm hands clutched at her shoulders, and his thumbs rubbed the flesh of her upper arms in a soft circular motion. At his nearness Anna felt a strange tremor shoot through her body, causing her breath to quicken.

Mistaking her trembling for shock at the memory of her near-drowning, David pulled her closer in his arms, his hands moving to caress her bare back comfortingly. It only made the tremors shaking her worse, and with a protest muffled against the large expanse of chest her face was pressed to, Anna began to struggle against his hard arms.

"Please, let me go. I don't want . . ."

As she spoke, Anna tilted her head back to look pleadingly up into his face. As soon as her eyes contacted his, she knew she had made a mistake, as she saw his narrow in sudden awareness.

"What don't you want, honey?" David whispered, his voice strangely husky.

Anna couldn't answer, lost in the depths of his darkening glance. Without her even being aware of it her struggles had stopped, and she studied his face almost compulsively. His skin was tanned to a warm, teak brown, with tiny lines fanning out from the corners of his eyes as if he spent a lot of time gazing toward distant, sun-filled horizons. His hair was midnight black and waved silkily around his head, its length long, but not too long, she thought inconsequentially. Her eyes moved from his to gaze in fascination at the strong column of his throat, mesmerized by the pulse beating riotously in its hollow. Tearing her eyes from that beating reminder of her own pulses throbbing unwillingly through her body, she was even more confused by the thick mat of black hair visible through the open collar of his shirt.

Her eyes moved to his mouth, the lips full and hard

with a sensual slant curving them rather mockingly, she thought. Her own lips trembled at the memory of that mouth covering hers, remembering the taste of the sea and the driving force of his own breath filling her lungs.

As Anna's eyes returned once again to his, her own dilated in fear as she read the expression upon his face, his head lowering inexorably toward her own . . . and her body stiffened in protest.

When he felt her tense, his large hand came from around her back to tilt her chin backward, his thumb caressing the wildly beating pulse in her own throat.

"Don't be afraid, I won't hurt you," he whispered, his words fading as his lips gently caressed her own.

At the touch of his mouth Anna's resistance melted as if it had never been. She shuddered as she felt his lips moving gently back and forth against hers. His thumb still probed maddeningly against her throat, and Anna was almost relieved when the soft pressure was removed, but not for long. Instead his hand moved to her cheek, and his finger coaxed the corner of her mouth downward. As she felt her lips parting, Anna jerked in arms which suddenly hardened viselike around her body when she felt the softness of his tongue first circling her lips and then entering her mouth slowly.

Anna wasn't conscious of anything but the sensations his kiss was arousing in her body, and without being aware of it her hands clutched at his shoulders, and her body automatically arched against his provocatively.

It seemed to be all the encouragement he needed as he lowered her body downward, his own weight pressing her down in the softness of the mattress. She felt as if she were drowning all over again and nearly gave herself up to the blissful sensations he was causing . . . her mind clouded with a desire never before felt.

A moan escaped her through their merging mouths as she felt his hand cupping her breast, his thumb circling the

38

hardening nipple. His mouth tore free from hers, and she gasped for air as his lips slipped easily over her throat to her breast. It was when she felt his tongue replacing his exploring thumb that she came to her senses with a jolt.

With a sob she grasped the dark thickness of his hair, forcing his now suckling mouth away from her breast. Her breath was tearing through her lungs in choking gasps, and she felt tears of reaction coursing down her cheeks.

"Don't . . . please, stop," she cried, trying frantically to lever herself backward and away from the weight of his body.

To Anna's surprise he let her go immediately, even going as far as to lift the blankets around her shivering form. She jumped in fear when she felt his hand against her face, but her eyes widened bemusedly as he gently wiped the back of his fingers against her cheeks, his hand shaking slightly as he removed her tears.

"Look at me, little one," he whispered, and Anna forced her lowered, shame-clouded eyes upward.

"I didn't mean that to happen, honey," he said softly, and Anna was amazed to see the passion fade from his face, to be replaced by an expression of regret. "I only meant to comfort you at first, but you were so damn lovely . . . Please believe me when I say I'm sorry for taking advantage of your vulnerability. I'm just a man, sweetheart, not a saint, and for a while there I thought you knew the score."

Anna looked at him numbly, her gaze questioning . . . and then full realization smote her. He had thought her experienced . . . thought through her own responses to him that she slept around! Oh, God! He had saved her life, taken care of her while she'd been unconscious. If he had wanted to take advantage of her, he'd had ample opportunity. Looking into his eyes she saw self-reproach clouding the shimmering green, and she felt total shame for what she'd driven him to do. It was all her fault!

39

Anna must have mumbled her last thought aloud, because David suddenly jumped up, raking his hands through his hair frustratedly.

"For God's sake, it wasn't your fault. You were already upset . . . and you're just a baby. I'm thirty-three, a hell of a lot more experienced at controlling my own emotions than you appear to be!" As he spoke he kept his back to her, searching through drawers enclosed within the wall opposite. Anna saw he had a shirt and a pair of jeans in his hand and felt a fresh surge of gratefulness for his consideration when she realized the clothes were for her.

"Please, don't blame yourself, David," she begged as he still kept his back turned toward her. "I'm not such a baby as you seem to think. I'm nearly twenty, after all. I have necked before, you know!"

Anna couldn't understand her own anger, which surged over her suddenly. He'd called her a baby for one thing, but what really upset her now was the fact that he wouldn't turn around. She was trying to make him feel better, and he was treating her like a pariah, for goodness sake! Anna saw his shoulders heave as he took several deep breaths, but at her words he gave a sardonic laugh which rippled through her, helping to fan her anger.

"Is that what you call it . . . necking? For God's sake, are you so inexperienced you don't realize I was almost at the point of no return? Necking hell . . . we were damn near going at it in earnest, you little fool!"

"I know you're ashamed, and so am I," she yelled back in hurt retaliation. "Does that mean I'm not fit to look at anymore? I . . . I've never . . . never felt like that with anyone before. I've never . . ."

"Don't you think I know that?" David cried, turning to face her finally. "If I'd turned around a few moments ago, little one . . . I'd have shocked hell out of you, but I don't expect you to understand what I'm talking about. What I am telling you is this," he snarled, throwing the clothes upon the bed. "If you don't get something on, and I mean right now . . . I won't be responsible for my actions!" With these words he strode purposefully from the cabin, and with a sob of hurt Anna heard his footsteps climbing toward the upper reaches of the cabin cruiser.

Anna's tear-blurred eyes noticed her dry bikini hanging over a chrome railing as she stumbled on shaking legs into the small cubicle which did service as a bathroom. Putting them on hurriedly, she noticed their softness against her skin. She was struck again by David's thoughtfulness, realizing they had been thoroughly washed of all traces of salt water. Washing and drying her face in the tiny basin, she found a comb in the mirrored cabin above and with shaking fingers repaired the ravages to her hair as best she could under the circumstances . . . grimacing at the stiffness of the usually silken soft tresses.

Returning to the main cabin, she donned the jeans and gray polyester shirt. Biting her lip in vexation, Anna held the pants up with one hand, for the waistline was nearly twice as large as her own. There was no way the darned things were going to stay up on their own, but she dreaded calling out to David for help. After what had passed between them just moments before, she couldn't stand the thought of facing him just yet!

With a small thud she sat down upon the edge of the bunk, staring down at her knees despairingly. How in the world, she thought with desolation, had she gotten herself into this mess? How could she have responded so wantonly to someone who was, after all, a complete stranger to her?

"Are you all right?"

Anna jumped at the sound of his voice, her head jerking up in surprise.

"Th . . . the pants won't stay up," she mumbled, once again lowering her head, avoiding his face, which looked at her in concern.

"Here, maybe this will help," he stated, removing his belt from around his own waist. "I'll cut a few notches to shorten it for you."

As he spoke he opened a drawer, and she saw him extract a pair of scissors, his deft fingers making new notches in the belt, and cutting off the end to shorten the length.

"Please . . . you're ruining your belt," Anna protested, but he only looked at her impatiently.

"Come over here. Let's see if it fits."

When she just stared at him dumbly, his expression softened. With a quick movement he went to her and gently lifted her from the bunk until she was standing close to him. As she felt his hands at her waist, fitting the belt through the loopholes of the jeans, his knuckles accidentally brushed against her bare skin, and she shivered in response.

"M . . . my name's Anna Mason," she blurted nervously, trying to cover up her reaction to his touch.

"Anna," he whispered, a question in his voice as he gently lifted her chin to gaze into her face. "That's a nice name . . . but I'll call you Ann."

"But I don't like the name Ann," she protested, pulling away from his hand and taking a nervous step backward, away from the magnetic force his body seemed to have for hers.

"It'll be my special name for you, honey. There's an old saying that when you save someone's life you become responsible for them. If that's true, then I should have earned the right to call you Ann."

"You don't have to be responsible for me," she retorted, her independent spirit insulted at the idea of being treated like a child.

Smiling at her angry look, he grabbed the mug of cold coffee and stepped into a little area beside the stairs which she now realized was a galley, complete with hotplate and what appeared to be an ice chest for storing perishables.

While she watched, he dumped the cold coffee in a stainless steel sink and rinsed the cup out thoroughly before refilling it from a rather battered pot on a butane stove.

Turning, he handed it to her. "Do you take anything in it?"

"No thank you . . . I drink it black," she replied, inhaling the aroma gratefully and cupping the warmth of the thick ceramic mug with cold fingers.

Walking carefully, she managed not to trip on the trailing ends of the baggy pair of jeans. She had attempted to cuff them earlier, but there was so much material, the cuffs wouldn't stay put.

David turned his head and laughed out loud when he saw her predicament. "Here, let me take care of those for you."

To Anna's horror David knelt down at her feet and with quick decisive movements began to shear the end of her jeans with the scissors. She knew from the feel of the material that they were practically new . . . but realized in time that there was no use protesting. This man would do whatever he thought right without hesitation . . . not stopping to think. She supposed some people were thinkers, planning pros and cons very carefully, and others were like David, just getting the job done with as little fuss as possible.

"Where are you staying?" he asked later as they sat on deck, replete after a very satisfying breakfast.

"I've rented a small cottage on the beach . . ." she replied.

"Where I found you swimming?"

"Yes, I just moved in yesterday afternoon."

"How long are you staying?"

"I've rented the cottage for a week," she replied, smiling at him shyly before taking a last swallow of coffee.

"Then I'll know where to find you, won't I?"

At his words and the expression in his eyes Anna

shivered, feeling a sense of inevitability wash over her. At that moment she knew, as he did, that their lives would be linked together . . . that this for them was just a beginning.

CHAPTER THREE

Anna's thoughts that day proved to be prophetic, and by the end of that week she was so in love with David that there seemed no beginning or ending to life without him.

She discovered that like herself David was rather a loner. Her gradual discovery of his character seemed to fill a need in her, as she filled his own needs. Together they became two halves of a whole, and when she knew her week was up and she would have to return to San Francisco, she didn't know how she could bear it! As it was, she didn't have to, for David decided to move to the city more or less permanently . . . staying in one of the hotels he owned that was located near the financial district and catered largely to visiting businessmen, with provisions for minor conventions.

They met often, their feelings intensifying, until one sultry August night after dining at his hotel suite Anna received the longed for proposal of marriage. Not wanting any delay, they were married in a civil ceremony two weeks later, and Anna's happiness knew no bounds. It had seemed so right . . . so good.

They bought a small house in Sausalito, and David took an interest in her photography, encouraging her to return to school. With his degree in oceanography complete he turned his businesses over to a board of directors, of which he remained in control.

For nearly a year Anna had been ideally happy, developing her artistic talents through photography and delighting in her relationship with David . . . especially the nights spent in his arms. Then the bubble burst, and Anna hadn't even realized it at the time. David's love of his chosen field was as intense as her own interest in taking better and better photographs . . . and she had encouraged him to go ahead and take a planned cruise which would give him the practical experience he needed. He was to be gone four months, and Anna, though she didn't know how she would survive that long without him, had wanted whatever would make David happy.

That last night together had been spent making love and talking about the future and making love again. She had gone to the docks early that morning to see him off, and she felt a part of her was dying as he sailed away from her. Somehow she had gotten through the next few weeks, filling her days with school and her nights with study . . . and writing to David.

It was nearly two months before she realized she was pregnant with David's child . . . and her happiness seemed complete. After confirming her pregnancy she sent a special delivery letter to David, for the oceanographical study had been extended to six months and she couldn't bear to wait. After sending the letter she waited daily for a reply, but none came. At first Anna wasn't too concerned, for David wasn't exactly on a regular mail route . . . and she'd received only two letters from him in all the time he'd been gone. But as her pregnancy advanced, so did her apprehension.

*   *   *

46

Anna had been driving to school when disaster struck with such terrible suddenness. One minute she had been turning a corner just a block away from the campus . . . and the next there was a jarring impact as another vehicle ran a red light and cannoned into the side of the car.

When she came to, she was in a hospital. They told her she'd been lucky, for the other driver had died before they could even extract him from the car . . . but Anna only had superficial injuries. They called it a miracle . . . but what kind of miracle took away the tiny life growing inside of her . . . ?

Suddenly Anna was back in the motel room, staring into the whiteness of her face in the mirror with one hand clutching her stomach in remembered agony. Sweat was beaded upon her forehead, and with a shaking hand she wiped it off.

She had never seen David again. Apparently he had come to the hospital and settled her bill . . . but he didn't even have the courage to face her with the knowledge that it was all over between them. He had used lawyers instead . . . leaving her the house, a payoff for services rendered.

For a long time she had refused to believe it. Remembering his gentleness, his professed love for her . . . how could he have callously walked out on her without a word, especially when she had just undergone the physical and mental agony of losing his child? How could any man do that to a woman who had loved him as much as she had?

Even now it was difficult for Anna to accept, but finally she had faced the fact that David was gone and was never coming back. After months of illness the acceptance came, and for a long while hatred had come too. Maybe the hatred had saved her sanity, and looking back Anna couldn't decide who she'd grieved for more, David, or their little baby girl she'd never even seen.

Now she had come full circle, or so it seemed . . . and

she could finally face David with her accusations as she had so often longed to do. But suddenly Anna knew she would only hurt herself by resurrecting all the old misery . . . and she was still too vulnerable to take the risk. Let David think his walking out on her hadn't mattered. At least it would save her pride, and where he was concerned . . . that's all there was left!

"You ready to go, Anna?" Carla asked, walking behind her and gathering up her things to take to the car.

"More than ready!" Anna exclaimed, smiling at Carla, who never suspected the long journey into the past from which she had just returned.

They loaded up the car and drove across the large courtyard to the motel restaurant. After eating breakfast Carla and Anna drove slowly out of Bakersfield, unsure of which direction to take to connect with Interstate 5 once again.

"Are you sure this freeway will get us there?"

"Pretty sure, Carla. We went quite a way out of the direct route last night and nothing looks familiar. At least we're going in the right direction . . . according to the map."

"Since when can either of us read a map?"

"Have faith," Anna laughed.

"If we don't get there soon, I'm going to faint from hunger," Carla complained several hours later.

"This is one time I've got to agree with you," Anna sighed, hunching her shoulders to try and relieve the nagging ache from between her shoulder blades.

If they'd had any sense, they would have stopped in San Fernando Valley a couple of hours back and had a meal. They had discussed stopping, but on the map Long Beach hadn't appeared to be more than an hour or so away. That would teach them not to trust maps, she told Carla with a laugh.

Finally they were drawing closer to Long Beach, and Anna carefully branched off, following the appropriate arrows. They had passed Hollywood just minutes before, and she had been so busy craning her neck and exclaiming over various famous landmarks that she had almost ended up in the wrong lane. From here on in she'd better pay attention to the signs, she scolded herself, or they would end up driving off the pier!

"Whew! I was beginning to wonder if we were ever going to make it," Carla exclaimed, when they finally arrived at shipside, for they had followed the *Queen Mary* signs only to end up lost on the docks.

"I know," Anna laughed. "How we could have missed anything this big is beyond me. Isn't she beautiful?"

Carla agreed, herself awestruck at the *Queen*'s size. They were in the parking lot, close to her berth, and in comparison with their car she was immense.

"Carla, we're going to have to wait for lunch. We're supposed to be checking in right now . . . and Mr. Curtis will be waiting for us."

"You're right. I completely forgot the time," Carla exclaimed, giving Anna a rueful grin.

Mr. Curtis had left instructions for them to pull up directly in front of the ship's entrance, which they did with due haste, for by now they could hear each other's tummies rumbling. Anna was doubtful about the advisability of this when she observed the many cars and buses with, it seemed, the same idea. How in the world was he supposed to spot them in this crowd.

As it turned out, Anna had worried needlessly. As soon as she pulled the car to a stop, Carla pointed toward a long flight of stairs leading up to the wharf area. There was Mr. Curtis, hurrying down the stairs toward them, with two uniformed stewards at his side.

Before they knew what had happened, the car was being unloaded and Mr. Curtis was leading them to the reception desk in the main lounge, assuring them of the safe conduct of their belongings to their rooms and even advising Anna of exactly where her car would be parked. Carla looked at Anna as they signed the register, a mocking quirk to her eyebrow.

"I thought I was efficient," she hissed. "That man makes me feel like a chicken with its head cut off!"

"Shhh, he'll hear you," Anna warned, successfully stifling her own laughter. She knew exactly how Carla felt, for even at the studio he'd had the same effect on her.

It certainly wasn't his appearance which gave them such a feeling of inferiority, she thought, studying him out of the corner of her eye as he explained some facet of the ship to Carla. He was only an inch or so above her own five feet six inches and as before was dressed in a dark suit and tie. He looked very staid and proper and, for a man, was rather skinny. No, it was his very busyness which was so offputting, she thought with a smile. Everything he did was so . . . quick.

Entering Lord Nelson's Restaurant a surprisingly short time later, considering all they had accomplished, Anna was full of nothing but admiration for Mr. Curtis's efficiency. While these thoughts were crossing her mind, he smiled at her rather shyly as she preceded him through the entrance. *He's really a dear,* she thought, returning his grin. *Why, I think he's as nervous about us as we are about him!*

Their meal was brought quickly, and as they ate, Mr. Curtis outlined for Anna the convention schedule and what would be expected of her. They discussed various procedure possibilities, and Anna catalogued the information in her mind, trying to put together a possible photographic format.

"Anna, this should be right up your alley. Remember those photographs you took of nursing homes for the aged last year?" Carla's eyes shone with fervor as she looked at Anna before turning to Mr. Curtis.

"Anna was on assignment for an organization which was trying to improve conditions in various nursing homes around the country. They wanted to have Anna take pictures of the kind of situations they were campaigning against, but they got more than they bargained for. She not only showed the deplorable conditions but also captured the spirit and pathos of the elderly, left behind by a world that no longer cared."

Anna laughed. "As you can see, Carla is not only an invaluable secretary, but also my biggest fan and staunchest ally."

"That appears to be true, Miss Mason," he smiled, looking seriously from Carla to Anna. "But it's not everyone who has the ability to inspire such devotion, you know."

"I should say not!" Carla exclaimed, giving Anna a reproving frown. "As a direct result of that publicity layout, Mr. Curtis, there was an outcry from people all over the country wanting to help in the cause."

"Yes, yes," he exclaimed eagerly. "That's just the kind of thing we want. Of course, it will be more difficult to capture those emotions because working with animals isn't the same as working with human beings, but if it's at all possible to achieve, we're sure you're the one to do it."

"I'll do my best."

"You always do your best, Anna," Carla retorted indignantly.

"I'm sure you will," Mr. Curtis smiled, picking up the check and walking with them to the cashier. "Now I suggest I leave you to get settled in. There'll be a table reserved for you at dinner, so I'll see you both then," he smiled, shaking both their hands before walking away.

After he departed, Anna and Carla walked down the long corridor to their rooms. Their footsteps were muffled by the long expanse of faded red carpeting crisscrossed with variegated leaf designs, a pattern popular many years ago. She couldn't help wondering how many years ago it had been laid, for though obviously well-worn in spots it was in extremely good condition.

The corridor itself was low-ceilinged, and the walls were almost completely made up of rich, mellow reddish wood. It was difficult to believe they were actually on board a ship at all, she thought. Though that wasn't entirely true, for there was an atmosphere composed of a combination of sights and smells, of lamps secured firmly to the walls, and maybe even of something left behind of the people who had sailed on her during her many years of service, she mused fancifully.

"Look, Anna," Carla exclaimed as they stepped over the raised threshold into their cabin. "This looks like a first-class cabin!"

"You're right, Carla. Look, we've even got two port-holes," she laughed.

There were twin beds in the room, and while Carla plopped upon one of them with a grateful sigh, Anna walked over to check their luggage and make sure her equipment was all right.

"Anna, you must be exhausted. Can't you do that later?"

"I just want to make sure nothing's missing, Carla," she replied, satisfied finally that everything appeared to be there.

"Mr. Curtis referred to our rooms . . . but it seems to me we're to share one. Look, my cases are over there in the corner," Carla remarked, yawning. "I guess we'd better check with the reception desk. When they handed us each a key, I just assumed they were for adjoining cabins. I guess we should have checked the numbers then, because I sure don't feel like walking all that way at the moment."

"Why bother, Carla? This cabin seems roomy enough for both of us. I don't mind sharing if you don't."

"It's all right with me," Carla replied, folding both arms

behind her head and snuggling her reclining body into a more comfortable position. "I was thinking of you."

"Why? You don't snore!" Anna laughed, turning away and glancing at the skyline from the porthole nearest her.

"I just thought that if you met some handsome stranger on board, you might want some privacy," she retorted wickedly.

At Carla's innocent remark Anna stiffened. A picture of David tore through her mind, his image as clear as if she'd seen him only yesterday. Would he have changed at all? Maybe his hair, once so rich and thick, would have receded, she thought hopefully. She tried to imagine David, at least the David she had known, without hair and with a thickening waistline, and failed utterly. Physically he had been superb, spending as much time actively as he could spare to keep himself in shape. Somehow she couldn't imagine David letting go and becoming over-weight, and with his body he would still be a damn sexy man, she thought savagely, even without a hair on his head!

Thoughts like that weren't helping her one little bit, she thought, turning from the porthole view with a taut jerk and walking over to sit on the edge of the matching twin. Carla was already asleep, and with a tired sigh she too re-clined on the bed. Closing her eyes determinedly, she rolled over onto her side, but sleep was elusive.

She tried to image what it must have been like to sail aboard the *Queen* in her heyday, with the sound of the waves lunging against her massive sides, and the roll of the ship as she fought through the plunging ocean.

David, with his love of the sea, must have had some-thing to do with the convention being held aboard the *Queen Mary*, she thought. Damn it! Why couldn't she stop thinking about him! If she didn't gain control of her thoughts now, she'd probably make a fool of herself in front of him . . . and that she had to avoid at all costs.

Why should she give him the satisfaction of sensing the wounds he'd left inside of her?

Would the knowledge give him satisfaction, though? The David she had thought she'd known all those years ago had hated to see anything suffer. He had been a gentle, considerate man and would never have needlessly caused anyone pain.

That's why she had tried so hard to contact him in those first weeks after losing the baby. All the lawyer would tell her was that he had left on another and more extensive oceanographical study and that he'd left instructions that under no circumstances was he to give her any information as to his whereabouts.

Remembering, Anna again cringed in shame. The lawyer had looked at her so pityingly, she rememberd, as he'd observed her whitened face and shaking hands. Still not recovered physically, she had even begged him to send David a letter, but he had refused, telling her David had instructed him against any type of correspondence.

God! If she could only go back again, how different things would be, she thought tearfully. Sitting up once again, she wiped the back of her hand over her cheek and shuddered as she remembered that first day, when David had done it for her. The feel of his knuckles wiping the tears from her cheeks came back to her and with it a remembered flash of desire. Who was she kidding, she thought savagely. If it were to be lived over again, those months with David, she doubted whether she would have been able to withstand the potency of his attraction. Just remembering the feel of his warm, hard flesh on hers left her trembling . . . and it had been five years!

Anna groaned aloud, looking nervously over at the sleeping Carla. Quietly she got up and found aspirin in her handbag, for her head was pounding with the force of a sledgehammer. Taking a glass from the top of the marble counter in the bathroom, she quickly dispensed of the pills, nearly gagging as they finally slid down past the nervous constriction in her throat.

Studying her white face in the mirror, her expression taut with tension, Anna clenched her hands at her sides in an attempt to repudiate the image in the glass. She looked an absolute wreck!

She had to get out of here or she'd go completely crazy, she thought, bending down and washing her face. The cool water against her skin partially calmed her, and with a determined tread she walked over to her equipment, removing her camera case from the pile and remembering to grab the case with extra film and filters. With a last glance at Carla she quietly closed the door behind her, and turned to walk quickly down the corridor to the freedom that beckoned on the shore.

The tide was receding, moving steadily back to be enfolded within itself as Anna walked slowly along the dampened sand. Wriggling her toes in the moistness, she swung her shoes in her hand, luxuriating in the coolness against her skin. As she moved, her feet made a soft sucking sound, and as the waves came in again to bathe them free of sand, tiny bubbles of water appeared in the indentations left behind, smoothing and forming the sand until it was once again pure and untouched.

Anna's legs ached from the long walk, and she moved further up on the sandy soil away from the water. Sitting down with a sigh of relief, she lowered her cases to lay beside her and wrapped her arms about her knees in an attempt to ward off the chill of the air. The weather was beautiful, the sky a brilliant blue as she gazed over the horizon, admiring the glint of sunlight glancing off the rolling, green-flecked foam and watching the many sailboats in the distance. They looked like a child's toys, bobbing about on the surface of the water, she thought with a smile of contentment.

Once again she rose to walk further along the shore.

The sight of the city of Long Beach in the distance was beautiful . . . but right now she didn't need people around her, for she needed time alone to recover her equilibrium and to strengthen her for the evening to come.

Breathing deeply of the salty tang in the air, Anna turned to begin the long walk back. Suddenly she stopped, her attention caught by a low recession in the ground to her left. Quickly she walked toward it, eagerness now in footsteps which had been lagging with tiredness just moments before.

It was! Her thoughts were exultant as she gazed down into the small tide pool left behind by the swiftly moving waters. Kneeling down, she observed the tiny sea creatures moving about in their own miniature ocean. This was just what she'd been looking for, she thought, her earlier depression forgotten in her eagerness to ready her camera.

Anna knew from repeated experience that she needed to find just the right camera angle to keep the effect she wanted, for the angle of view has a great deal to do with the color of the water achieved in the finished picture.

Studying the quiet pool, Anna bit her lip indecisively. The sun was beginning to lower, and she was fully aware she had to be quick, for the ocean's colors were perceived chiefly from the reflection of the sky. Quickly she fitted a polarizer onto her camera; it was an invaluable aid in penetrating the surface of quiet pools to reveal details within.

Taking a series of shots from various angles, Anna leaned back with a sense of accomplishment warming her.

"Hello, Ann!"

At the sound of the deep, slightly raspy voice she knew so well, Anna stiffened. *Oh, God!* She wasn't ready for this meeting . . . not now, not like this! Extremely conscious of her far-from-immaculate appearance, which didn't help her confidence one little bit, Anna slowly rose to her feet.

Turning, she faced David across a distance of a few

feet, not responding to his greeting. At her first sight of him it was as if she were being hurled into the past, for it seemed he hadn't changed at all. Her breath felt constricted in her chest, and with a hand visibly shaking she brushed her wind-tossed hair out of her eyes.

"It's been a long time, Ann," he said, his voice harsher than she remembered it. "Aren't you going to say hello to your husband, or is it to be a silent war?"

At his mocking words Anna flinched. In the beginning his refusal to legalize their separation had given her hope . . . and later she'd been so despondent, it had ceased to matter. Reverting to her maiden name, over the years she had become used to thinking of herself as single. She felt a flicker of unease at the fact that David should feel it necessary to remind her of their married status.

Turning silently away from him, she began shoving her precious camera into its case with frantic haste.

"You've changed, Ann!"

At his harsh exclamation Anna turned to face him, a disdainful expression in her eyes.

"What did you expect, David, time to stand still? You've not exactly been left untouched yourself," she sneered.

"I don't mean physically and you know it. You're still a damn beautiful woman, as you're well aware."

"Then what did you mean, David? Am I expected to read your mind?" Anna retorted. "There was a time when I wanted to, but not any longer!"

Her words ringing in her ears, Anna began to walk quickly away, only to be pulled to a stop by his firm hand closing over her arm, the force of his grip causing her to gasp in pain.

"I'm sorry, I didn't mean to hurt you."

"It seems like I've heard those words before!"

"Damn it, Ann," he exclaimed angrily. "We've got to talk."

"I don't see why, unless you want to talk about a divorce," she replied tiredly, all the fight leaving her. "Anything else we had to say to each other was said years ago. We're strangers now . . . and I guess we always were."

"What the hell do you mean by that remark?"

"We never really knew each other, David . . . we only thought we did. Our lives touched briefly, but that's all there was to it. You might refer to it as temporary insanity . . . at least that's how it appears to me."

"Temporary, hell," he snarled, pulling her resisting body close against the muscular hardness of his. "That little pulse beating in your throat always gave you away, Ann. It's beating like mad against my hand right now. Does this feel temporary?"

Her eyes widening in reaction, Anna gazed into the glittering green of his own. Against her will her body seemed to curve softly into his. She began to moisten her dry lips with her tongue, but stopped when she saw his eyes following the movement intently.

"Let me go, David," she demanded, her voice quiet in the gathering shadows of early evening.

"Why should I, Anna? If you don't want to talk, then we won't, but there's one form of communication we've always been good at," he whispered, lowering his head purposefully.

At the first touch of his mouth on hers she gasped aloud, her breath mingling with his. There was no preparatory gentleness in his kiss, just a hard, sensual demand as his mouth expertly parted hers.

God in Heaven, had she ever hoped these feelings were dead? Madness gripped her, and at the touch of his tongue lightly caressing the soft inner flesh of her mouth, any thoughts of resistance fled. Her camera slipped unheeded to the ground, and she felt a moan rise in her throat at the intensity of her feelings.

It had been so long, so very long! Convulsively she

clutched the silken white shirt that covered his arms, but even though she clung to him with her remaining strength, she felt her knees buckle under her.

With a feeling of panic Anna felt the sand cool against her back as David, never breaking their kiss, lowered her to the ground. She felt his weight pressing her down and with a feeling of disgust at the wantonness of her response began to struggle.

"God . . . don't fight me, Ann," he groaned against her lips. "It's been so long . . ."

As his words echoed her earlier thoughts, Anna stiffened. She felt his hand move against her blouse, his fingers slowly undoing the buttons. His mouth was once more ravaging hers, stifling her protest, and she was again thrust into a vortex of desire as she felt her blouse part beneath his hands and a cooling rush of air on her heated flesh.

For comfort while driving she'd chosen not to wear a bra, and now she cursed herself for the omission. She felt his indrawn gasp of surprise, which soon turned into an aching moan of pleasure, as his hand unexpectedly encountered the smoothness of her breast.

Anna felt she would die from the exquisite agony of the feelings shooting through her at the touch of his hands. There was no hiding her arousal as her nipple hardened, pressing into his palm. As his head raised from her throbbing lips, she knew he could read the desire clouding her eyes.

His eyes lowered, following the movements of his hand on her breast before once again looking up into her own. Slowly he lifted himself to a kneeling position beside her. His breath was causing his chest to heave in massive gasps as he began unbuttoning his shirt . . . his gaze locked with hers.

There was no question in his look, for he already knew the answer, she thought, closing her eyes in shame. She wanted him as a man dying of thirst craves water . . .

and she was almost maddened by his slowness. He was doing it deliberately, she thought, biting her lip in agony. Making her wait, building the tension in her, until like a mindless idiot she was ready to give him whatever he asked of her.

After all this time to just step back into her life and think he could start from where he left off was more than she could take. Taking him completely by surprise, Anna rolled away from the temptation of his body, which she knew could end the agony knotting her stomach and leave her satiated with pleasure. Muffling a sob, she moved farther away from him, turning her back and trying to refasten her blouse with shaking fingers.

She could hear David behind her, rising to his feet . . . but he made no attempt to come closer. Taking a deep breath for control, she walked over to her discarded camera, placing the strap over her shoulder and carrying her shoes. Her movements were hurried in her attempt to get away from him, and she avoided looking in his direction.

"For God's sake, put your shoes on, Ann," he growled, raking his hand through his hair. "I'm not going to rape you!"

Looking at him numbly, the retaliation she wanted to utter locked in her throat, she complied. It was very dark now, and all she would need was an injured foot to add to her problems. The sooner she could escape from him, the better off she would be, she thought hysterically, once again rising to her feet.

"Come on," he demanded. "Let's get out of here!"

"I'm not going anywhere with you, David," she retorted, shocked by his attempted authority over her.

"I hate to disagree with you, Ann . . . but you are coming with me. My car's parked a short distance away, and I'm not letting you walk back alone in the dark."

"I'm a grown woman," she shouted, rage at his high-handed attitude spearing through her. "I'm perfectly capable of walking back, dark or not!"

"If I hadn't delayed you, it wouldn't be dark," he retorted sarcastically.

At his words Anna was thankful for the darkness, feeling her face flush hotly. What was it about him that brought out the very best in her emotions and at the same time the very worst? There didn't seem to be any comfortable middle ground with David, and painfully she remembered the intimacies of mind and spirit they'd shared in the past.

Knowing it was useless to argue with him once his mind was made up, Anna followed him to his car. She slid onto the seat stiffly, not turning her head to glance at him when he entered to sit beside her in the matching bucket seat of the low-slung Ferrari.

The close, luxurious confines of the car added an unwanted intimacy, and Anna tried to hide the fact that her body was shivering. She felt him looking at her before attempting to start the car, his gaze so intent it seemed to burn over her flesh.

With a muttered curse David reached behind the seat, pulling out a dark blue cashmere sweater and handing it to her with impatient movements.

"Put it on before I do it myself," he snarled, starting the car and accelerating swiftly, the force of the suddenly moving vehicle causing her head to jerk backward against the headrest. Silently Anna placed the sweater around her trembling shoulders, clutching the soft edges convulsively against her still-throbbing breasts.

With a feeling of alarm Anna suddenly realized they were heading away from the direction of the *Queen Mary*, moving instead toward the town itself. Swallowing with difficulty, Anna braced herself to speak . . . but no words passed her lips. Wetting her lips nervously, she glanced over at David, only to find him once again watching her mouth intently, his eyes meeting hers with a glittering promise in them.

"Cat got your tongue?" David mocked softly, turning his head back to the increased traffic of the city.

"Where are we going, David? I want to go back to the ship."

"I told you we needed to talk, Ann," he remarked, negotiating traffic, his hands skillful and sure upon the steering wheel.

"W . . . we can talk tonight at dinner," she retorted, cursing herself for the slight tremor in her voice.

"Were I to take you back, you'd scurry away to your cabin like the devil were at your heels, Ann. If it weren't for your roommate . . . I might agree with your suggestion," he replied.

"How did you know someone was sharing my cabin?"

David didn't answer, and at his silence a shiver sliced through her, sending a frisson of unease through her body. About to question him again, she felt frustrated when at that moment David pulled the car over to the curb in front of a small restaurant. Avoiding her eyes, he lifted himself from the driver's seat and walked around the car to open the door for her.

Stubbornly Anna remained where she was, her body eloquent of her disapproval. With a gasp she felt his hand on her arm as he nearly pulled her from her seat.

"Damn it! I'm not in the mood to argue with you, Ann," he grimaced, slamming the door shut and almost pulling her along the walk to the restaurant entrance.

"Let me go!"

"I will when you stop acting like a child," he remarked, just as quietly as if he were passing the time of day.

Anna wanted to tear her hair, scream . . . do anything to relieve the pent-up frustration she was feeling, but another couple walked up behind them, and the moment was lost. He wouldn't get her to lower her dignity to the extent of behaving like a shrew in public, she thought, her mouth a taut line of anger.

Without a word David seated her in a booth for two located in the bar section of the restaurant. As he walked up to order their drinks, Anna slid out, glaring at his amused expression as he watched her stride angrily to the door of the ladies room.

CHAPTER FOUR

Once inside, Anna walked over to the washbasin, sluicing her face with cool water and patting it dry with a soft white paper towel. Taking her comb from her purse, she tugged it through her tangled curls with savage motions. Her fingers shook as she applied a clear, colorless gloss to her lips, and she gritted her teeth in an attempt to stop their shaking.

Feeling somewhat better, Anna turned and started toward the door. With her hand touching the coldness of the metal handle she hesitated, taking in a deep breath of air. With a determined tilt to her chin, her mouth set in an angry line, she returned to the bar . . . and David.

"Feel better?" David questioned softly as she slid into the seat opposite him. There was a time, she remembered unwillingly, when they would have shared the same side of the booth, unwilling to be more than a few inches from each other. Looking up at David, she saw a mocking glint in his sea-green eyes, telling her he was as aware of that memory as she was.

"David, I want to know how you knew Carla was with me," she demanded.

Silence greeted her question, while David's large hand was caressing the stem of his half-full glass.

"David, I'm warning you," she began, only to stop short at the expression in his eyes. They warned her not to push him too far, for with his dark head thrown back, his eyes hardening into cold, chilling slits in his face, she could read a freezing anger in every line of his taut body.

Anna quickly lowered her eyes to her own drink, taking a large swallow of the white wine David had ordered, in an attempt to bolster her sagging courage. She was appalled to feel her eyes moistening. Tilting her glass, she drained the rest of the wine recklessly, nearly choking on its dry sweetness.

"Take it easy, Ann!"

"May I have another, please?"

"Why, so you can accuse me of getting you drunk?"

"David, please don't . . ."

With a muffled curse he jumped from his seat, striding with angry steps over to the bar. Watching him, she felt tension coiling even more strongly through her body. Oh, God! She couldn't take much more of this!

With the wine once more in front of her she fiddled with the stem of the glass. David's warning about getting her drunk must have hit home, she thought, fighting against giving in to a hysterical urge to laugh.

"Were you told the name of the man heading this convention?"

As his question penetrated the mists of her jumbled thoughts, her head jerked up to stare at him in surprise.

"No. All that matters is doing what I'm being paid for. I never thought to ask."

"You mean you take pictures without looking into the organizations you're working for?" David inquired disbelievingly. "How can you get the results required without some foreknowledge of who you're representing?"

"I didn't mean that," she retorted, lowering her voice

65

when she saw the inquiring looks being sent their way from people in the booth opposite.

"Then explain what you did mean," he demanded, his voice dripping icily.

"What business is it of yours anyway?"

"Can't you guess?"

Anna stiffened in alarm at his softly worded question, and her eyes dilated in emotion as she looked up into the harshness of his face.

"Y . . . you," she whispered, her face whitening.

"Yes, honey," he retorted mockingly. "I'm the man heading this convention. I'm the one, for all intents and purposes, you've got to contend with."

Her voice a thin thread of sound, Anna asked, "Who arranged for me to come here?"

When there was no answer to her question, Anna closed her eyes in agony. Oh, God! He had arranged for her to come here . . . he was enjoying playing with her like a cat with a helpless mouse. She should have guessed . . . should have known that there was just too much coincidence in their meeting. What tortured her most . . . was why? Why, after walking away from her five years ago, had David gone to all this trouble to see her again? Why?

She must have whispered the word aloud, for David's voice suddenly cut into her thoughts.

"Do you really want to know why, Ann?" There was a warning note in his voice she couldn't ignore, but with renewed courage she mutely nodded an affirmative.

"Because the thought of you has haunted me for years," he answered, his words pouring from his lips in a torrent. "Your mouth, your skin under my hands, the way you used to gasp and wriggle beneath me when we made love until you nearly drove me insane. Sex has never been so good for me, either before you or after. You might say this is a last attempt to lay your ghost, Ann!"

At the coarseness of his remark Anna closed her eyes,

trying to close the image of him from her consciousness as easily as she could from her sight. David had changed more than she had at first realized. He was much harder than he used to be, and she sensed a vein of cruelty in him which hadn't been there five years ago. Well, she was harder and stronger now, too . . . and she was damned if she'd let him get away with his devious plans. She'd show him how difficult it would be to exorcise her ghost!

No! If he thought she'd just hop into bed with him, he had another think coming, she vowed. He could live on his memories the way he had forced her to do. There was no way she was going to begin again with him . . . not even if it meant the ending of her career. She remembered what she'd gone through when he finally finished with her last time . . . and she knew she couldn't go through that again without coming completely apart at the seams!

"Aren't you going to make any cutting little remarks, Ann?" David sneered, his hand reaching across the table to grip hers in a vise of steel she found impossible to break.

"Why should I give you the satisfaction, David? I haven't unpacked yet . . . I can be out of here in an hour."

"Have you forgotten that contract you signed, honey?"

"That isn't worth the paper it was written on under the circumstances," she retorted, pulling her hand free, finally, from the warmth of his clasp.

Sitting back indolently, he studied her intently across the width of the table, a cruel smile playing around the corner of his mouth.

"Isn't it, Ann," he whispered. "Are you sure you read all of the clauses?"

"W . . . what do you mean, David?" she stammered, feeling a terrible sense of foreboding gripping her.

"I anticipated this eventuality, Ann," he remarked, his words clipped and almost emotionless . . . as if he were

67

discussing a business deal which didn't affect him unduly, she thought despairingly.

"Get to the point, David," she demanded, her voice hoarse as she stared into his eyes, which looked back at her with an almost malevolent glare.

"All right, I'll get to the point," he said, emphasizing the last word angrily. "If you default in any way from this assignment, Ann . . . you leave yourself open for a suit which will cost you your studio . . . and nearly anything else of value you possess before you manage to pay it off."

"Damn you! You can't be serious," she cried, clenching her fists under the table, the urge to physically hit out at him so strong, it made her stomach churn.

"I'm as serious as I've ever been, Ann . . . so don't count on any mercy or weakening from me. I am what life has made me, honey . . . and what I want, I take," he snarled.

"You threw me over," she cried hysterically, no longer caring who overheard. "Why decide now that you want me?"

With a curse David swiftly stood up, draining the last of his drink in one large swallow. Nervously Anna rose and followed his striding figure out of the restaurant. The cool evening air whipped her face into flushed, tingling life as she negotiated the short distance to the car, her own legs feeling wooden beneath her.

They drove the short distance to the *Queen Mary* in total silence. Any words between them seemed anticlimactic, Anna thought, biting her lip angrily. She was amazed that she could still feel anger . . . in fact she wondered how she could feel anything at all. A coldness was settling around her heart, freezing her into a stiff caricature of the woman she had thought herself. Now she seemed to be all mixed up with the girl she used to be, and the two halves were fighting a war inside of her.

The David she had known would never have acted in

this cruel, uncaring way, she thought, feeling tears choking her throat. No, that wasn't entirely true, she corrected herself automatically. There must have always been this side to his nature; he just had been careful never to let her see it. But it had been there or else he wouldn't have done to her what he had. It obviously wasn't in him to feel love . . . just desire, and she wished fervently that he'd never come back into her life.

What perverted streak in his nature would cause him to decide after all these years to take once again what he'd so callously thrown away before? If he had said one word about being sorry . . . Anna knew, with a sense of self-disgust at her own weakness, that she would have believed him because she would have so desperately wanted to.

But he wasn't sorry . . . not at all. He never even referred to his leaving her, and when she tried to bring it up, he had stormed out of the restaurant in a fury. It was as if there was something bottled up inside of him . . . something he didn't want to admit even to himself.

David parked the car, and Anna glanced at him out of the corner of her eyes when he made no move to leave. His hands were clenched around the steering wheel as if he were making a terrific effort to control the anger seething inside of him, his knuckles white from the force of his grip.

When he turned to meet her furtive glance, Anna saw a muscle pulse in the side of his jaw as if his teeth were clenched. His eyes seemed to darken, and Anna swallowed with difficulty, cursing herself inwardly for her timidity.

"Are you still planning to leave?"

At his question Anna bit her lip indecisively. The old David would have never followed through on his threat to ruin her, but it seemed as if she would have to learn to read his character all over again. This wasn't the same man she had known so intimately in the past . . . he was like a stranger to her. Taking a deep breath, Anna decided to force his hand.

"Yes, I'll leave tonight, David . . . and under the circumstances I won't waste any time doing it!"

"Have you thought of the other people you're going to hurt by running out on this assignment, Ann?"

"What are you talking about? Just what are you threatening me with, David?"

"Your secretary . . . Carla? I understand she supports two children with her salary alone. It's going to put quite a strain on her if she suddenly finds herself jobless, isn't it? And the other photographer in your business—I believe his name is Allan Simpson? He's gradually put quite a bit of money into equipment, hasn't he?"

"Y . . . you've had me investigated? You had the nerve . . ."

"Yes," he snarled, turning his body toward hers. "I know everything there is to know about you, Ann . . . and I'll use whatever methods I have to in order to achieve my aims."

Shrinking against the door, Anna stared into his granite face, her eyes widening in horror at what she read there. She was trapped, and she knew it. Oh, she knew Carla wouldn't have much difficulty in finding another job . . . but he had her cornered when he mentioned Al . . . who had steadily been buying into the business, aiming eventually at a full partnership. Al worked hard and had invested heavily over the years . . . and she owed him her loyalty. Damn him! He knew she was beaten; she could tell by the slow smile she saw gradually wiping the harshness, if not the coldness, from his face.

"Where do we go from here?" Anna mumbled woodenly.

"Don't freeze up on me completely, Ann," he mocked. "I have no intention of taking you back to my cabin . . .

not yet. I don't have the time," he laughed, tapping his watch.

"I'd fight you anyway, David. If you think I'll just jump into bed with you, you're crazy!" As she spoke, Anna glared at him across the intervening space, his laughter infuriating her.

"Calm down," he ordered, his mouth firming. "If you want lies whispered in your ears, then I'll give them to you, when the time is right. For now just remember that I'm your boss, and I'll be the man you answer to for your time while you're here!"

Jumping from the car, Anna turned to yell at him through the open door, her body shaking with the intensity of her feelings.

"Go to hell!"

As he watched her running from him, David's hand slowly unclenched its grip on the steering wheel. Slowly he passed his shaking fingers over his face, closing his eyes in agony.

"I've already been there, honey," he whispered hollowly. "Dear God! You're the one who sent me!"

By the time Anna reached the cabin, she had finally managed to gain some measure of control over the sporadic trembling of her body. She had run from the car until reaching the main lobby . . . run until she'd felt her lungs would burst. As her feet carried her swiftly, so too did her thoughts threaten to sweep out of control.

It was only the startled stares she received that finally caused her to slow her steps. She must have seemed like a wild woman as she ran in from outside, she thought grimly, taking a deeply calming breath before opening the door and stepping inside.

"Anna," Carla exclaimed, emerging from the bathroom with hurried steps.

"You act as if I'd been gone for a year, Carla," Anna

71

said, her smile feeling strange . . . lips moving stiffly in what seemed a caricature of the real thing. Seeing Carla's answering smile, she sighed with relief. At least Carla didn't seem to suspect anything was wrong, and she could be grateful for small miracles.

"Hey, dinner's in forty-five minutes, Anna. Why are you just standing in the middle of the room like a statue? You don't have to be nervous, honey. You'll make a super impression on this Mr. Carmichael, especially in that gold evening gown you brought with you. Anyway, your looks alone would be enough," Carla laughed, grimacing at her own reflection in the mirror before glancing down disparagingly at her outdated blue chiffon.

"You know you look lovely, you nut," Anna argued, laying out her own dress and staring down at it doubtfully. Mind finally made up, she snatched it up again, smoothing out its silken folds regretfully as she returned it to its hanger.

Swiveling around on her seat Carla exclaimed; "What are you doing?"

"I've decided not to wear the gold after all," she answered, averting her face while rummaging in her overnight case for her toilet articles.

"I borrowed your shampoo, Anna. It's in the shower," Carla stated, her eyes puzzled as she studied Anna's nearly frantic movements. "Why ever not?"

"Why not what?"

"Why aren't you going to wear your new dress, Anna? I thought you bought it especially for our first night," Carla questioned, her eyes following Anna's retreating figure.

"I guess I'm just not in the mood tonight, that's all," Anna replied from the bathroom . . . feeling safer away from Carla's discerning eyes.

"I think you're nuts," Carla exclaimed disgustedly. "You look like a million dollars in that dress, and you know it. I would have loved to have bought that green jersey we saw in the window, and you'd better believe I'd have worn it, too!"

"Why didn't you buy it, Carla? I would have paid for it, and you could have paid me back," Anna called through the partially closed bathroom door. She stood nakedly poised, waiting until she heard Carla's reply to turn on the shower.

"Oh, I could have bought it, but Gary's shooting up so fast he practically needs a new wardrobe, and I'd promised Susan a party dress for the school Valentine dance next month. You know how important a new party dress can seem to a twelve-year-old!"

"Why didn't you tell me that at the store?" Anna groaned, sticking her head around the door and glaring at Carla. "For goodness sake . . . I'd have given you the damn thing as a present. You deserve something for yourself once in a while too, Carla . . . and I can't remember the last time you bought yourself anything new."

"That's why I didn't say anything, because I knew you'd insist on buying it for me and I couldn't let you. I'd have felt like a scrounge until I paid you back—you know how I am."

"Too proud by half, you stubborn woman," Anna said, shaking her head reprovingly at her friend. "Be warned, though," Anna smiled. "Your birthday's coming up in a couple of months . . . and if I chose to get you a dress, you won't be able to say a thing about it!"

"But, Anna!" Carla began, only to find the door shut firmly on her protest, the sound of the shower preventing further speech.

That was handled rather well, Anna thought smugly, smiling at the memory of the disconcerted expression on Carla's face. Lathering quickly, she felt the grime and tensions melting away under the warmth of the water, filling her with renewed energy and a feeling of strength. The

73

strength she would need in double measure if she were going to get through tonight.

After drying haphazardly Anna wrapped the towel sarong-wise around herself before plugging in her electric hair dryer. As the warm blower tumbled her hair riotously around her head, she couldn't help laughing at herself, one-handedly trying to squeeze toothpaste on her brush after removing the cap with her teeth. A lot could be said for giving yourself extra time to stop and think instead of getting nervous knots in the stomach from rushing around. If it hadn't been for David . . . she'd have had more than enough time to get ready, she thought, bad temper getting the best of her resolution to stay calm and collected.

Satisfied with her appearance, she left the bathroom, gasping as she noticed the time. Oh, Lord! She still had to get her evening clothes on, not to mention checking her equipment! To be late tonight of all nights would be the final indignity, and she only had ten minutes before dinner began. She'd never make it in time!

Frantically Anna began rummaging through her cases. Where was her camera? She'd prepared it especially for tonight with the correct filters, and she could have sworn she'd placed it on top. A white slip of paper caught her eye, and with a frown she grasped it, her fingers shaking with nervous tension, making it nearly impossible to read. Thank God! It was from Carla . . . letting her know all equipment was checked and would be waiting downstairs at their table. With a sigh of relief Anna ran to the closet, pulling out a black jersey trouser suit and quickly stepping into it. Grabbing a pair of anklet nylons and pulling them on, she slipped into sling-backed silver sandals. Now all she needed was her silver evening bag and she was ready.

Bless Carla! She always managed to smooth the path with her usual efficient thoughtfulness, Anna thought, as she hurried down the hall. Anna couldn't help but envy

Carla's ability in that direction . . . for no matter how hard she tried, she usually managed to become flustered when she was working under a deadline. There just didn't always seem enough time to accomplish everything, and she was usually at her wits end when Carla stepped into the breach to smooth things out for her. No matter what Carla thought about being efficient, to Anna it seemed little short of a miracle . . . the ability to organize one's schedule into a smoothly flowing pattern.

"I don't believe you made it on time," quipped Carla, grinning up into Anna's flushed face.

"Thanks to you," Anna smiled, her gaze nervously drawn toward the empty seats at their table.

"All I did was check your equipment for you. After all, I need to do something to justify my presence."

"You need to do nothing of the sort, and you know it," Anna retorted, sitting down with a sigh of relief. "Where's the big man?"

"My, my! We do have our claws sharpened and ready, don't we?"

"I don't know what you're talking about, Carla," Anna frowned, lifting her chin in an unconsciously haughty gesture.

"Now . . . there's no need to jump on your hobbyhorse. We know each other a little too well for that!"

Carla was right . . . she was acting bitchy, overreacting to an innocent remark in that stupid way. Her nerves were getting the better of her common sense, and if she wasn't careful, she'd give herself away completely.

At that thought Anna clenched her hand around her water glass, sipping from it with a concentration the simple action didn't merit. What if it wasn't up to her at all? What if David referred to their earlier relationship? Oh, God! She could just imagine Carla's questions if that happened. Somehow she had to keep David from blurting everything out. It was bad enough having to cope with him without facing Carla's knowing eyes also. *It just isn't fair,* she thought, self-pity clouding her eyes.

To distract her thoughts Anna let her eyes wander around the room. Her gaze wandered up the smoothly polished wooden columns toward the center, and she looked in awe at a crystal model of the *Queen Mary* on the far wall. It was a large, extremely decorative map . . . and must have been quite something when all lit up.

"I see you're admiring the décor."

She didn't need to see Carla's face to guess at her friend's awestruck reaction to David's presence. She herself had felt as if she'd been touched by an electric wire when the deep tones of his voice resounded from just behind her chair.

"Aren't you going to introduce me, Ann?" David asked, his voice as indolently mocking as his body as he walked around Carla's chair to sit directly opposite Anna.

Gulping nervously, she slid her glance to Carla's accusing face, not quite meeting her eyes.

"Carla, this is Mr. Carmichael. W . . . we met earlier on the beach. Mr. Carmichael, my friend and assistant, Carla Peterson."

Glancing nervously at Carla while she made the introduction, Anna wryly noticed the almost awed expression on her friend's face, understanding completely the emotions reflected there as David turned the full force of his smile upon Carla's unsuspecting head. That smile could be devastating, as she well remembered . . .

"Glad to meet you, Mr. Carmichael," Carla enthused, her voice slightly breathless. "I didn't know you and Anna had already met," she continued, sending an accusing glance toward Anna.

Anna's eyes moved swiftly toward David. *Oh, please . . . don't do this to me,* she thought, her eyes pleading with him across the table. She saw the rapier gleam harden to deadly coldness, his lids narrowing over their

76

flashing green brilliance. His look encompassed her, causing her to shiver in response. His eyes widened as he noticed that slight, almost imperceptible movement, only to suddenly narrow again as he noticed the agitated twisting of her white-knuckled fingers in her lap.

"As Miss Mason said . . . we met on the beach," he drawled, turning to smile at Carla. "It probably slipped her mind."

There had been a small hesitation in his voice before he said beach, and Anna knew he wasn't referring to their earlier meeting . . . but to that day so long ago when he'd pulled her unconscious body from the water. She closed her eyes, not realizing she'd been holding her breath until she expelled it torturously from her lungs.

"You called her Ann a little while ago," Carla smiled, glancing swiftly from David to Anna.

"I can't help thinking of her as Ann," he laughed, his eyes lazily inspecting Anna's tense body with maddening thoroughness. "Anna . . . Ann! Yes, the name suits her. She reminds me of someone I knew . . . rather well . . . a long time ago. With your permission, Ann?"

Damn him! His voice was dripping sex, and she almost groaned aloud at the expression on Carla's face. She had seen that matchmaking gleam before, but it had never really bothered her, the tendency Carla had of trying to set her up with some unattached male. This, though, was entirely different . . . and she shot David a malevolent glance from under her brows.

"With my permission . . . what?" Anna's voice dripped sweetness. She wasn't stupid enough to give herself away to Carla by objecting to his use of her name; that would be playing right into his hands.

"That depends on you," he rasped seductively, his eyes burning into her, seeming to sear her with his glance . . . and causing her eyes to widen in response. She gasped in reaction to his verbal love-play, hearing her own choked

77

breath echoed by Carla, herself affected by the obvious vibrations seething just below the surface. He was leaving no doubt in anyone's mind, she thought savagely, seeing the almost embarrassed glance Carla gave her.

"Excuse me, I think I'll get a few preliminary shots," she mumbled, jumping up and grabbing her camera, afraid if she stayed any longer, she would explode.

Just the action of taking pictures soothed her, and gradually she became engrossed in her work. There were about two hundred people here, she guessed, and as the first speaker rose, Anna was caught by the expressions on their faces. They were intent, a suppressed enthusiasm and excitement pervading the throng. If she could just catch that atmosphere on film . . . that energy flowing from the voice of the speaker and rebounding upon the crowd!

With a sigh of completion she slowly took the last of the film. As she made her way back to their table, her feet began to lag. She wished she were anywhere but here, and her stomach tightened as she spotted David's dark head, a quick spasm of jealousy spearing through her unexpectedly as she noticed how attentively he was looking at Carla. She must be crazy, she thought in disgust.

Anna sat down abruptly, placing her camera back in its case with shaking fingers. Looking up, she caught the mocking glance David was giving her and immediately made an effort to control the slightly sulky expression she knew she was wearing.

"Do you think you got what you needed?" Carla questioned, smiling at Anna good-naturedly.

"Not yet . . . but she will," David whispered under his breath, his eyes alive with hidden innuendo.

"Yes, I think so," she replied quickly, hoping Carla hadn't caught on to David's mocking undertone.

As Carla went on talking, apparently oblivious to any undercurrents in the conversation, Anna shot David a murderous glance, seething when all she received in return

78

was a mocking tilt of one dark eyebrow. Really, the man was going to come to a violent end if he didn't stop baiting her like this!

The relief she felt when their dinner arrived was so great, she could have reached over and kissed the waiter. Carla had been giving her puzzled looks from time to time, as if aware of her preoccupation. How could Carla help being suspicious, Anna thought, with herself contributing to the conversation with inane monosyllables while David just sat there, obviously eating her with his eyes!

As that thought jumped unbidden into her mind, Anna felt a slow flush stain her cheeks. Looking down at her half-empty plate, she moved the food around . . . anything to give her an excuse to keep her head lowered. She tried to concentrate on the silverware, the placement of the food . . . anything to wipe out the sensuousness of the thoughts torturing her. That mouth, softened with passion . . . seeking and finding the hidden woman's places on her body . . . driving her closer and closer to the edge of madness . . .

As if she were driven, Anna raised her eyes to David's, watching almost mesmerized as his widened in an inner knowledge of her thoughts, darkening now with a passion-glazed look which mingled with her own. Her gaze moved down to his strong brown throat, and she raised her hand to defensively cover the pulsing in her own as she noticed the telltale throbbing beneath his skin. Closing her eyes in a purely defensive gesture, she once again lowered her head. The silence was almost tangible, and for the life of her she couldn't think how to break it!

Anna didn't know whether she could stand much more of this, and relief surged through her when she heard David's swiftly indrawn breath and his muttered good night. Shocked by his abrupt departure, Anna felt a surge of uneasiness as she watched his lean, pantherish stride eating up the distance.

"Well! He certainly appeared to be in a hurry all of a sudden," Carla exclaimed, turning bewildered eyes toward Anna. "Was it something I said?"

"N . . . no! I'm sure we had nothing at all to do with his decision to leave. He's a very busy man and probably remembered something urgent that required his attention."

Anna knew she was rambling, but she couldn't seem to stop herself. She could feel a flush rising once again in her face and took a quick sip of coffee, trying to appear as relaxed as possible. She wasn't succeeding very well if Carla's suspicious, narrow-eyed glance was anything to go by.

"He's certainly a very handsome man, isn't he?"

"Y . . . yes," Anna answered warily, distrustful of Carla's innocent tone of voice.

"And really built . . . wouldn't you say?"

"I guess so, if you like muscular men," Anna replied, beginning to feel deliberately goaded as she looked at the mocking expression on Carla's face.

"That raspy huskiness in his voice is enough to send shivers down any woman's spine, but I guess you've already realized that . . . hmmm?"

Finally Anna could hold back no longer. Carefully placing her coffee cup back in its saucer, she looked Carla right in the eyes, her lips set in a mutinous line.

"What are you getting at?"

"You know very well what I'm implying, Anna," Carla laughed. "Why, the signals the two of you were sending across the table nearly gave me powder burns!"

"Y . . . you're imagining things, Carla," she sputtered. "You know me well enough by now to know I don't allow men to come on . . . or you should."

"Honey, don't get so upset," Carla comforted, suddenly appalled by the whiteness of Anna's face. "I know you're not like that. For goodness sake, I was just teasing you. Anyway, just because you're fastidious in your relation-

ships with men doesn't mean you've joined a religious order. It's only natural to be attracted . . . and who knows,
it might be good for you to have a little fling."

"Carla," Anna whispered, staring at her friend as if
she'd never seen her before, until Carla dropped her eyes
in embarrassment.

"Well, it's true," Carla muttered rather belligerently.

"Th . . . there's nothing like that . . . nor will there be
if I have anything to say about it."

"Maybe you won't."

"What do you mean by that?"

"Just that he didn't seem to me the type of man to take
no for an answer," grinned Carla unrepentantly.

"Well, he'll just have to learn," Anna exclaimed, nearly
gnashing her teeth in frustration at the way the conversation was going.

Suddenly a waiter appeared at her side, and Anna
almost groaned with relief at the diversion his presence
created.

"Miss Mason?"

"I'm Miss Mason," Anna replied, looking up into his
smiling face and giving him a reserved smile in return.

"Mr. Carmichael wishes to meet with you to discuss tomorrow's schedule. He regrets the necessity of cutting into
the rest of your evening but asks that you meet with him
an hour from now in his suite."

"Please inform Mr. Carmichael that I'll meet with him
tomorrow morning before breakfast to discuss any details
he may think necessary," she replied coolly.

"Mr. Carmichael foresaw your objections, Miss Mason.
He'll be tied up at a meeting during the morning until
called upon to speak."

"I'm sorry," Anna replied apologetically. "It's impossible
for me to meet with Mr. Carmichael tonight. Give him my
answer please."

After the waiter departed, Anna raised her eyes to Carla's mocking face.

"Well, what are you waiting for?" Anna remarked, her head tilted at a belligerent angle. "Go on, say it!"

"All right," Carla smiled, winking her eye provocatively. "I told you so."

"Did that make you feel any better?"

"I'd feel a lot better if you'd agreed to go!"

Anna felt like gritting her teeth at Carla's outrageous remark. Little did Carla know what she'd be letting herself in for if she agreed to see David alone in his suite! He was going to be absolutely livid when he received her message, but she had no other choice. Under other circumstances, with any other boss, she'd have thought nothing of going to his suite to finalize details . . . but not with David. Nothing would induce her to be alone with him, not under any conditions!

"Well, since you're not meeting the boss, how about a stroll around the promenade deck before bed?"

CHAPTER FIVE

Anna agreed, and suiting actions to words, they were shortly walking slowly around the well-lit deck of the ship. The night air was cool, with a slight breeze wafting the smell of the ocean deliciously around them. The lights in the distance looked like a fairyland as they gazed across at the city of Long Beach.

Anna couldn't help but be glad that this wonderful old ship, so much a part of history, had been loved and revered enough to be given a permanent home when her usefulness was over.

Before her mother died, especially toward the end of her illness when her mind would wander, she would tell Anna stories of how her father returned from World War II on this very ship. Anna was too young to remember him, for he'd been killed in an automobile accident just months after her birth. It made her angry to think of how her father had survived four years of fighting overseas . . . only to find his life taken by a drunken driver coming home from a party. Now it felt strange to think he had walked these very decks.

Suddenly Carla smothered a yawn. "God, I'm tired. I

feel as if today has been a week long. I'm for bed, are you coming?"

"I guess I'd better," Anna replied, following Carla through one of the entrances. They traversed the wide corridor swiftly, this time paying scant attention to the many shops on both sides of the lobby and heading directly for the stairs. Soon they were on B deck, and as they reached the foyer which stretched the whole width of the ship, Anna stiffened when she heard her name called. She didn't need to be told whom the voice belonged to, for there was Mr. Curtis hurrying toward them. She looked at Carla and just shrugged her shoulders at the worried expression on Carla's face.

"Miss Mason, I'm glad I caught you. I was just on my way to your room with a message."

"Two guesses who from," Carla whispered, nudging Anna with her elbow.

Frowning warningly at Carla, Anna turned to Mr. Curtis. "A message, Mr. Curtis? It wouldn't be from Mr. Carmichael would it?"

"Why, yes . . ." he began, his expression hesitant.

"I've already received the message, Mr. Curtis," Anna interrupted, not caring at this moment if she appeared rude. "Mr. Carmichael's already received my answer."

"Miss Mason," Mr. Curtis blustered. "There must be some mistake. I just spoke with Mr. Carmichael. He told me I was to go to your cabin and bring you to him without delay. Believe me, it was not in the nature of a request."

"Mr. Curtis, I don't see why it's so important that I talk with Mr. Carmichael tonight. Wouldn't tomorrow be soon enough?"

"I believe the matter's urgent, Miss Mason. I know you must be tired, but I'm sure Mr. Carmichael won't take up too much of your time."

"I'll bet," mumbled Carla suggestively.

"I beg your pardon?"

At the bewildered look on his face Anna bit her lip in indecision. Damn David! It was just like him to throw his weight around in this manner. He had this poor man practically tied up in knots trying to do his bidding . . . and she didn't have the heart to add to his worries.

"Mr. Curtis, would you mind waiting here for me? I'd like to go back to my room first. Can I meet you in about fifteen minutes?"

A smile of relief spread over his face as he nodded his reply, walking quickly away to sit on the padded circular bench in the middle of the foyer.

Back in their room Carla sat on her bed, watching in amusement as Anna paced furiously across the floor. She never said a word as Anna quickly stripped off her evening wear to replace it with an old pair of wool slacks and a rather shapeless gold cable-knit sweater she'd brought along for her forays on the beach. Carla coughed delicately behind her hand, and Anna wanted to strangle her . . . knowing she was probably hiding a smile of amusement at her expense.

"I'd like to know what's so funny about this whole situation!" Anna growled, running a brush angrily through her tousled curls, throwing down the brush in disgust and turning to glare at Carla.

"Oh, Anna," Carla choked. "I told you he wasn't the kind of man to take no for an answer."

"That's just what he'll get from me," Anna raged. "Who does he think he is?"

Suddenly Carla's face sobered. "He's the boss, remember."

"That doesn't give him the right to demand my presence at this hour of the night."

"Now, Anna. I know I've been teasing you all evening about Mr. Carmichael . . . but that doesn't mean I'm right in my crazy suppositions. He may really have urgent business to discuss . . . So please, calm down. You can't go and see him in a fury or you just might put your foot in it!"

Sitting down on the matching twin, Anna ran a shaking hand through her hair, surprised to feel slight moisture beading her forehead. Impatiently she wiped it off with the back of her hand, taking a few deeply calming breaths.

Carla was right as usual . . . at least as far as she knew. Anna herself wasn't in any doubt as to David's motives, but she couldn't let Carla know that. Anyway, she'd be playing right into David's hands if she showed up screaming like a shrew. No, the best way to handle this was to appear calm and collected . . . and very, very businesslike. She would take a notebook and pencil just to add to the businesslike atmosphere, she thought with a smile tugging at the corners of her mouth, and if he got within three feet of her . . . she'd stab him with it!

"Anna, I don't like that look in your eye!"

"Carla," she mocked, widening her eyes innocently. "I don't know what you mean."

"You know very well what I mean, you wretch," Carla retorted, sitting up with a jerk. "All I can say is . . . don't!"

"Don't worry, I'm not planning anything drastic."

"I hope not, Anna. David Carmichael wouldn't be a man I'd care to cross."

Anna frowned absent-mindedly at Carla, letting her words sink in deep. No . . . David wasn't the kind of man you could cross, and wasn't that exactly what she'd vowed—to his face no less—to do? A notebook and pencil, old sweater and slacks . . . they might give her a momentary confidence, but would she stand a chance if David decided to exert the power she knew he had over her? No . . . especially since David was as aware of her reaction to him as she was. She'd left him in no doubt, not after that episode on the beach. God, how had she been crazy enough, even momentarily, to melt at his touch the way she had! It had been as if for a brief moment of time in his arms the intervening years had melted away. Why had she let herself forget even for a little while the agony he'd caused her in the past? Was she so starved sexually that she'd welcome the lovemaking of a man she should hate?

With a wave of good-bye and a thumbs up sign for Carla, Anna left their cabin to seek out Mr. Curtis . . . notebook and pencil dutifully clutched in her hand. The questions she'd been asking herself continued to haunt her as she walked slowly down the long corridor.

If she were sexually starved, wouldn't she have gone to bed with other men to satisfy her cravings? After all, she was a grown woman, a consenting adult . . . and this was a pretty permissive society. Why then had she held back . . . until the moment David once again held her? Other women were able to receive satisfaction from any number of men . . . so what made her so different, she wondered.

Anna allowed none of these thoughts to show on her face as she greeted Mr. Curtis, walking with him to the main deck with as much cool dignity as she could muster from her trembling body. Approaching the door to the suite, Anna moistened her suddenly dry lips with her tongue. Damn him for ever coming into her life! If she was, as she suspected, a one-man woman . . . it would have been better if the sea had forever cradled her lifeless body; for he had given her the breath of life . . . only to take it away with him when he'd left her!

Mr. Curtis knocked briefly and when there was no reply, opened the door. Taking a deep breath, she stepped nervously over the threshold, relief flooding through her when she preceded him into a small but elegant sitting room . . . which was mercifully free of David's overpowering presence.

"If you'll just take a seat for a moment, Miss Mason?"

87

"Thank you," she replied distantly, unable to summon even a travesty of a smile. "W . . . where are you going?"

Anna nearly choked at the childishness of her question, not needing his swiftly appraising glance at her to know how undignified her words sounded. Why in the world was she losing her grip like this? She was a grown woman, not some simple-minded child afraid of a bogey-man. She had to stop letting her fear of David control her actions to this extent!

As Mr. Curtis left the room through a connecting door set against a wall completely encased in the rich wood prevalent throughout the ship, he at first reassured her, letting her know he was going to apprise Mr. Carmichael of her presence.

Little did he know, she thought sarcastically, that far from reassuring her his words only caused more turmoil inside her already tense body. With a groan she jumped to her feet, wrapping her arms defensively around her body as she paced the thickly carpeted floor. Reaching the door through which they had entered, she could feel her fingers tingling with the urge to turn the handle and escape before it was too late. Fighting the urge, she turned, leaning against the wall and surveyed the room with brooding eyes.

She couldn't help responding to the elegant décor, enjoying the way the subdued lighting cast seductively soft shadows against the wood before blending peacefully with the richly golden carpeting. The décor and decorative accents of the lovely room provided a cross section of the Art Deco style. There was functional elegance, and she couldn't help but admire the brilliant use of space. All in all it consisted of restrained modernism with the result of subdued elegance which still retained an atmosphere of restfulness and comfort. It reminded her of a picture she'd seen in a magazine of a dignified English country home. Even though she now resided in California, that very

British charm and grace still cloaked the *Queen Mary* in an enchanting beauty all her own. Standing on the shore of Long Beach, a person might feel the urge to sing "God Bless America," but standing on these decks and looking out at the same scenery, one would be more apt to sing "God Save the Queen," she thought with a smile.

"What are you playing at, Ann?"

With a gasp Anna's body jerked upright, her fists clenching at her sides in a helpless movement. She looked across the room at him, and felt emotion choking her as she unwillingly registered his tall, muscular elegance as he walked indolently across the room. Black slacks stretched tautly across his thighs, and her mouth felt dry as she noted the way they clung lovingly to powerfully rippling muscles.

Forcefully tearing her eyes away, she felt even more flustered when she encountered his knowing eyes, watching mesmerized as they slowly enveloped her body in a searing glance.

"I asked you a question, Ann," he stated, at last breaking the tense silence.

"I . . . I don't know what you mean," she evaded, lowering her eyes to the white shirt covering his chest before looking away nervously upon becoming aware of the black mat of hair faintly showing through the silk.

"I sent you a message at ten o'clock . . . a message you ignored," he growled, turning angry eyes in her direction. "Are you still trying to pretend you don't know what I'm getting at?"

Her chin rising at the sneer in his voice, she replied with as much dignity as she could muster. "I just didn't see anything that had to be discussed at this hour. Nothing that couldn't wait until morning," she replied, her eyes widening at the growing expression of anger he was making no attempt to hide. She felt real apprehension licking through her nervous system and drew a shaking breath,

89

hating herself for waiting tamely for his wrath to fall instead of telling him exactly what she thought of his summons.

"For God's sake, come over here and sit down," he rasped, the force of his words slicing through her temple, where she was beginning to feel a dull throb pulsing.

"I . . . I'm perfectly all right where I am," she retorted, her voice sounding maddeningly timid even to her own ears. She could imagine how it must sound to him!

"I said . . . come over here and sit down," he whispered, making an obvious effort at controlling his temper. "We have things to discuss, Ann . . . and I'm damned if I'll have you standing by the door obviously ready to cut and run at the first excuse you can think of!"

Anna was fighting a losing battle, and she knew it. She was behaving childishly, and the scorn on his face was emphasizing that fact all too clearly, she thought . . . her mouth tightening mutinously as she walked across the room. Seating herself on the edge of the large, straight-backed easy chair he indicated, she fought against recoiling when he stretched his legs indolently after sitting beside her in a matching chair, apparently at his ease.

"There's just one thing we have to get clear," he began, his words clipped and coldly precise. "When I issue an order to you or any other employee, I expect to be obeyed, Ann . . . immediately and without question. Is that clear?"

"I'm not just some lowly slave you can order about when you choose, David," she began hotly, only to feel her words cut off abruptly at the expression on his face. Dear God, he looked as if he wanted to do her injury, and once more she felt a strange shiver of fear lace up her spine. Odd, she thought, clenching her hands into tight fists and closing her lips together tightly to prevent crying out. She'd been aware since seeing him again on the beach that she feared David's power over her emotions

90

. . . but she had just begun to realize that there was more to her feelings than that. She sensed a violence in him held firmly in check . . . but there all the same! There was a darkness in him, something buried deeply which occasionally burned in his eyes when he looked at her . . . a depth to his character which hadn't been there five years ago.

"Might I remind you, Ann, that I'm paying a high price for your services. That gives me the right to order your presence any damn time I choose!"

Deep in her own thoughts, she was a first bewildered at David's words, but finally her churning thoughts subsided and his meaning came through loud and clear.

"I just want to make clear to you that you're paying for my services as a photographer . . . and as such you'll get the best I have to give, David. If you imagine my fees enable you to receive anything else from me, though, then you'd better think again," she breathed warningly, her own fury increasing at the mockery in his eyes.

"Scruples at this late date, Ann?" David sneered, his voice coldly insulting. "It seems to me I paid well for your services once!"

Anna gasped at his words, her eyes closing in agony at the pain they were inflicting upon wounds which, she knew now for a certainty, had never fully healed. With the cry of a wounded animal she jumped up, nearly stumbling in her haste to reach the door.

"Damn you, you're not going anywhere until I say so," he snarled, grabbing her arm painfully and jerking her around to face him.

"Let me go!"

"Stop struggling, you little wildcat," he ordered, his arms enclosing her fighting body like steel bands, drawing her close against his muscular frame in an attempt to lessen her movements.

"I never touched a penny of that money!" Anna yelled, jerking her head back and glaring into his eyes. "It's all there any time you'd care to collect it, damn you. To me that money's as foul as you make me feel . . . and if you think I would have lowered myself to your standards by touching a penny of it, then you never knew me at all!"

All the while she was spitting her fury at him, Anna had been twisting and turning in his arms, her anger and shame making it possible for her to fight the attraction he held for her. Pain seared her, for his words showed her clearly how he'd thought of their marriage. All those months she'd been sure of his love for her, and he had only been amusing himself, playing the loving husband. What right had he to act as if he hated her? She was the one with the right to hate!

That was the root of the trouble, she thought, staring into his face as if seeing him for the first time. Even with him looking at her with such anger and contempt, his face set in ruggedly harsh lines, his arms hurting her with the force of his grip . . . even after the horrible things he'd just said to her . . . she couldn't hate him. She'd given him too much of herself that was irretrievable, too much passionate adoration, for her to accept him as he was now.

Suddenly Anna stiffened, for David was looking at her in a way she knew well . . . too well. She briefly renewed her struggles, only to stop when she realized that all she was accomplishing was an even closer, more sensual contact with the aroused hardness of his body.

David left her in no doubt as to the reality of his needs, slowly moving his hands down her back until he cradled her hips, his eyes never leaving hers as he sensuously pressed himself against her. She closed her eyes against the darkening passion in his, memories of other moments spent in his arms making a mockery of her resistance.

Her hands clutched his shoulders as his mouth began a languorous exploration of her face, his lips caressing her heated flesh with softly fluttering movements, maddening her with elusive promise.

"David, no!"

"You know you don't mean that," he whispered, his lips teasing the corner of her mouth.

"I . . . I do," she moaned, her heart pounding so hard she couldn't help but wonder if he could feel its frantic beat against his chest and know that she lied.

His mouth was driving her crazy, making her yearn for his full possession of her throbbing lips, and with a moan, despising herself for her weakness, she turned blindly toward the elusive torment. But David held back, accepting her kiss coldly, his body rigid and unresponsive. Oh, God! This was his way of punishing her for her denial of him. He meant to show her how little control she possessed and how little she herself could affect him.

Gathering together her scattered senses with as much will power as she could muster, Anna began pulling away from him. He was too strong, though, and she realized swiftly that until he chose to release her she was a helpless captive in his arms.

Her mouth, still burning from contact with his, was the only part of her David allowed her to move away . . . and she felt bewildered. Finally gathering her courage, she threw back her head and looked into his eyes questioningly . . . but what she saw in their depths froze the words in her throat.

Never had she seen an expression which frightened her as much as David's . . . a look of such raw lust and tormenting desire, it left her breathless. There was something else, and it was this that froze the blood in her veins.

She had told herself that David acted as if he hated and despised her, but until this moment had never truly believed her own thoughts. Now, seeing his eyes narrow at the sudden whiteness of her face, a wolfish grin sprawled insolently across his mouth, Anna was more afraid than she'd ever been in her life.

"David, don't . . . please don't," she moaned, twisting

her head to evade his mouth, only to feel it settle at the throbbing pulse in her throat while one hand insidiously slid past the waistband of her slacks, leaving a burning trail of sensation down her back. She squirmed against the forceful descent of his hard fingers, but David was determined to have his way, eventually kneading and smoothing the rounded flesh of her buttocks.

"Tell me you want me," he whispered, his tongue and teeth feasting upon her vulnerable neck and earlobe.

"N . . . not like this, David," she sobbed, tears beginning to flow down her cheeks, becoming a torrent as he ignored her plea, his mouth moving even more hotly upon her skin, his other hand lifting beneath her sweater to fumble for the clasp of her bra.

David's breath was coming from him in massive gasps, his chest heaving against her. She despaired as she felt the elastic fastening snap beneath his suddenly ruthless fingers . . . and his hand immediately slid around her rib cage, sliding under the now useless covering and clasping her breast painfully.

"Tell me how you want it, honey," he moaned, his words becoming lost against her mouth. "Just don't try to tell me you don't want this as much as I do, because I won't believe you." He laughed deep in his throat, his palm gently caressing the flowering hardness of her nipple. "Your mouth is saying one thing, Ann . . . but your body says quite another."

Anna fought down a moan as his hands moved sensuously against her heated flesh, determined to fight him with the only weapon left to her . . . passivity. She fought the shivers of delight spearing through her at his touch, but as his mouth once more moved on hers, his tongue coaxing her lips apart to enable him to explore her mouth with abandonment, she knew she was losing.

Grasping at straws, Anna tore her lips away from the ravishment of his mouth.

"Mr. Curtis . . . he said he'd be back," she gasped.

"There's a separate exit from the bedroom . . . he won't be back."

"You can't be sure. Th . . . this isn't the right time, David," she pleaded, playing for time.

"He knows better than to interrupt, Ann," he replied arrogantly. "I'd almost forgotten how beautiful you are," he breathed huskily, having put the time to good use by removing her sweater and bra.

By then Anna was in an almost drugged state, too overwrought emotionally to offer more than a token resistance, but his words suddenly tortured her brain. How many times, she wondered bitterly, had Mr. Curtis quietly made himself scarce while David indulged in late night "appointments"? Business, hell! The only business David had on his mind was the appeasement of his lust . . . and if she gave in to him, she would despise herself even more than he despised her already!

Her tears were drying on her cheeks, the flow stopping abruptly as a new idea, born from the depths of her desperation, came to her. Wrapping her arms around his neck, she swayed against him, beginning her own slow seduction. Her mouth played along his tightly clenched jawline, the tip of her tongue licking against the bristly hardness of his cheek.

"Mmm . . . I like that, honey," he moaned, moving his head to allow her nibbling mouth further access to the hard column of his neck. "At least you've stopped crying."

"My tears didn't seem to bother you at the time," she pouted, raising her head to look up at him. Her tongue snaked out to moisten her lips teasingly.

His eyes following the movement, David groaned:

"Do you know what you're doing to me, you little witch?"

"I . . . I've got a good idea," she whispered, arching her body against him.

Voraciously David's mouth fastened onto hers, hungrily demanding a response. Eyes tightly shut, Anna gave him what he was seeking, kissing him back with fervor equal to his own. Almost . . . almost she forgot her earlier determination, her body betraying her once again until she wanted nothing more than to be in his arms no matter what the circumstances . . . but a last burst of sanity halted her traitorous surrender.

She had to act now before it was too late! Withdrawing from his kiss with unbelievable effort, Anna gingerly rubbed the area around her mouth, looking at him ruefully.

"My skin feels like it's on fire," she remarked, her voice husky.

David looked at her with feverish eyes, his gaze then moving down her body slowly. Pulling away from her to afford himself a better glimpse of her golden skin, he then looked down at himself before raising his eyes to hers once more, smiling wickedly at her blush. "You're not the only one on fire . . . but I get your meaning," he sighed, rubbing his hand along the redness of her face caused by his late evening stubble.

"Come on," he ordered abruptly, raking a shaking hand through his hair while he fought for control.

"W . . . where are you taking me?"

"Where do you think," he mocked, dragging her through the connecting door and into his bedroom. The room was furnished very similarly to hers except for the double bed in its center. Anna nervously tore her eyes away . . . but apparently not soon enough. She gasped as David lifted her in his arms, striding across the room and depositing her on the mattress.

Straightening, he looked down at her, his eyes devouring her voluptuous charms, and Anna couldn't control her shiver of awareness.

"D . . . David, aren't you going to shave?" Anna's

voice was a thin thread of sound, her hands grasping his as they began tugging impatiently at the waistband of her slacks.

"I want to see every damn inch of you first," he murmured softly, a rueful smile tugging at the corners of his mouth. "You're right, though. I'm not sure I'd stop once I'd succeeded in stripping you . . . and you know it, you little devil." A laugh hovered in the air above her as David once more ran his hand raspingly against his face. "You never did like my bristles . . . I should have remembered to shave earlier, but it's your fault anyway."

"My fault?"

"I was too angry to see straight," he admitted, some of the anger returning to his eyes as he straightened completely, moving away from the bed without looking at her.

Relief was flooding through her . . . but it was a relief mingled with regret. For a while David had seemed to have forgotten his enmity . . . and it had almost been like before. Her ploy was working, only she wished it hadn't been preceded by a return of his coldness.

"Take off your clothes and get into bed," he muttered, once more raking her with a frigid glance. "I'll be back in a moment to collect the first installment!"

As soon as she heard the buzz of his razor, Anna jumped from his bed, her feet flying across the carpet, taking her into the sitting room. With frantic haste she donned her sweater, not bothering with the ruined bra but just stuffing it in her purse.

Later, sobs tore at her as she leaned weakly outside the door of her room, but she fought them back, muffling her choked gasps with her hand. Finally gaining some measure of control, Anna wiped the tears from her cheeks. She hoped Carla was asleep, for she didn't feel she could cope with any explanations at the moment. Thank God Carla was here, for she knew that if she'd been alone, David would have followed her and finished what he'd started.

As she quietly pushed the door open, Anna expelled her breath in a sigh of relief. She could hear Carla's even breathing from the darkness of the room, and with slow movements, like a thief in the night, she moved toward her own bed. Stripping off her clothes and dropping them across the foot of the bed in uncharacteristic untidiness, Anna slid between the sheets. She felt disoriented, as if she didn't belong here at all . . . almost like being a part of the present but knowing she really belonged in the past.

Smiling at the foolishness of her thoughts, she pulled the covers around her body in a defensive gesture, wanting to protect herself from all unpleasantness. She was tired, so very tired!

Much to her surprise the next day went swiftly, and though she dreaded another summons from David . . . none came. As she worked, she was able to put him from her mind only briefly, for his face kept coming between her and the activities going on around her.

The convention was in full swing, chairs replacing last evening's tables in the first-class dining room. The speakers were becoming more impassioned as time went on, and she could feel the tension building in the room.

They were speaking out against the yearly slaughter of the humpbacked whale . . . and several times Anna found herself stopping her work to listen, enthralled, an unusual occurrence for her. It wasn't so strange, really . . . for she'd always supported the Greenpeace movement, as well as this organization, which worked closely with them.

Anna remembered reading that every nineteen minutes a great whale dies in agony at the hands of men, and for what? To produce lipstick, shoe polish, cosmetics, and grease . . . products which can be produced from synthetic or vegetable sources at comparable cost.

Anna had supported the save-the-whales campaign for sentimental reasons, not logical ones. Mainly it had come about because she'd once seen a whale dead upon the shore. She'd joined the small crowd gathered around the great beast, and had felt unutterably sad that such a magnificent creature should die with so little dignity.

There was much conjecture as to why the whale chose death in such a fashion . . . and a young man standing beside her had remarked that possibly she was a female, who had lost her young. He seemed knowledgeable on the subject, telling Anna that being mammals, whales didn't belong solely to the sea, for they were air-breathing. When they had their young, the mothers tended them, even hlping them to the surface to breathe . . . until the babies were able to survive alone.

As he explained, Anna had felt tears choking her. Looking down into the face of the whale, she couldn't help marveling at how human it looked. Oh, not feature-wise . . . but even dead the whale seemed to retain a look of intelligence. Learning from the young man about what good care whales took of their babies, Anna felt a sense of affinity steal over her. He went on to explain that when a young whale lost its life, its parents quite often went crazy with grief. Remembering how she had wanted to die after losing her baby, Anna came to the conclusion, after further study, that with its large brain the whale quite possibly was extremely intelligent and able to feel very human emotions.

The more she read, the more she felt the slaughter of whales was morally wrong as well as unnecessary. Every species, she found, was on the U. S. government's endangered list . . . and some might soon only exist in the pages of history books.

Unlike other creatures, whales mate for life. The blue whale, she remembered—the largest creature ever to inhabit this planet—has been fully protected for over twelve years . . . and yet shown no signs of biological recovery. So few are left that males and females can't even find each other to mate. That comparison had touched her deeply, and once again she had identified with the whale. How terrible to have to wander through the depths alone . . . always seeking fulfillment.

With a jerk of surprise Anna brought herself back from her reveries, tensing as she saw David approaching the podium. His long, sleek stride seemed to eat up the distance with little effort on his part. He passed quite close to her and, as he did, seemed to look right through her. Anna closed her eyes, biting her lip at the harshness of that glance, knowing as surely as if he'd spoken aloud that it wasn't over between them.

With surprise Anna realized that as a speaker, David was superb, and she found herself listening to his speech intently.

"Ours is a water world," he began quietly, the subdued dignity of his voice capturing his audience from the very beginning. "It is seventy-eight percent ocean, and whales help regulate the ecological balance upon which we depend. Up to eighty percent of our oxygen is produced by one-celled oceanic plants called plankton. The plankton are eaten by tiny shrimplike creatures called krill; which in turn are eaten by the great whales. By eliminating the whales we are removing a natural restraint on the krill population. As their numbers expand, they eat the plankton we depend upon for our oxygen. A few years from now, if the composition of the atmosphere changes for the worse," he warned, his face harsh with the intensity of his feelings, "we may be sorry that we exterminated the whales . . . but by then it will be too late!"

A surge of pride washed over her as David continued talking knowledgeably, his words concise and his examples clear. This was the greatest change in him, she mused . . . for he handled himself with a confidence and expertise far greater than the old David would have.

His appearance surely didn't do him any harm either, she thought wryly, turning to look at the rapt faces of the women in the audience. She couldn't blame them, for in a dark suit, a pale gold shirt emphasizing the bronze of his skin above the darker gold tie, flecks of gray at his temples a startling contrast to the blackness of his hair, he looked not only handsome but terribly distinguished.

Anna was just one of the crowd herself, staring up at him and feeling a tightening in her stomach. If they thought he looked good now, she thought with a grimace, they should have seen him as he'd been last night! Today he was every inch the learned oceanographer . . . but last night he'd appeared hotly masculine, a superb male animal.

Jumping nervously from the applause ringing out around her, her eyes met David's briefly as he stepped down from the platform. She knew her expression was bewildered, and as she saw the knowing gleam in his eyes, she realized her expression at the moment of being pulled back from her thoughts must have mirrored the desire she'd felt last night. Oh, God! Why was she always at such a disadvantage with him? Why did he seem to be able to read her mind at the most inconvenient moments?

Turning away, Anna sought out Carla, feeling the need to put the width of the room between herself and David. She felt his eyes following her as she moved away, and was very grateful for the fact that it would be impossible for him to get to her. There were people all around him, attempting to gain his attention and throwing questions at him which demanded answers. She smiled, for his frustration was apparent. As he registered the smile, it faltered and died . . . for there was a warning glint on his face which seemed to be in the nature of a threat.

CHAPTER SIX

Finally locating Carla toward the entrance, Anna expelled her breath in a sigh of relief. She was using Carla as a shield, and she knew it, but she didn't care. At least Carla's presence afforded her some measure of protection . . . and unashamedly she was determined to take full advantage!

"Anna, wasn't he wonderful?" Carla enthused, smiling as Anna took a seat next to her.

"Oh," she replied, attempting a nonchalance she was far from feeling. "Do you mean Mr. Carmichael?"

"Yes I mean Mr. Carmichael," Carla imitated, shaking her head in disgust at Anna's obvious evasiveness.

"Yes, he's quite a good speaker," she remarked, not quite meeting her friend's eyes. "Actually I was really too busy to pay much attention," she lied.

"You were rather later than I'd expected last night," Carla remarked blandly. "Did the meeting go all right?"

"Ummm . . . yes," Anna answered, trying to control the flush which threatened. "I'd say it went entirely as expected."

"That sounds businesslike," Carla mused, searching

Anna's face intently. "Didn't he make even one little pass? If not, I'm going to be terribly disappointed in our Mr. Carmichael," she laughed, the knowing look on her face making Anna cringe.

"Now, I couldn't have that, Carla," David's mocking voice spoke from just beside them.

Anna's eyes closed, mortified that David should have heard Carla's thoughtless words. Her own skin prickled with awareness, as it always seemed to whenever he was close to her.

"M . . . Mr. Carmichael," Carla gasped, her face reflecting her embarrassment. "I didn't mean . . ."

Anna couldn't avoid thinking that it was entirely Carla's fault if she were embarrassed, and she was darned if she was going to make it easier for her. It was just like David, who always had had the soft-footed grace of a cat, to sneak up on them like that.

Much to Anna's annoyance David moved around behind her, and she stiffened when she felt his cool hands softly massaging her shoulders.

"Don't worry, Carla . . . you weren't that far off base," he murmured suggestively, the tip of one finger caressing Anna's taut jawline. When she pulled away from his mocking touch, she heard his laugh rumble deep in his chest. "Even if she did run away just when our . . . discussion . . . was getting interesting," he concluded outrageously.

"David," she choked warningly, forgetting the more formal mode of address in her anger, but quickly becoming aware of her mistake when she noticed the expression on Carla's face.

Damn! Now the fat's in the fire, she thought, biting her lip in vexation. Carla's look was reproachful, obviously blaming Anna for not telling her the whole truth; but what really disturbed her was the smile on Carla's face as she turned her eyes toward David.

It was frustrating sitting here and not being able to see David. Carla appeared to be indulging in some silent form of communication with him, judging by the fleeting shadows of expression crossing her mobile face . . . and she couldn't help a small sliver of resentment. She felt like the proverbial child who was never picked to play on anyone's team, or the little girl who stands on the sidelines at a dance. Well! She'd leave them alone then . . . and David could talk until Carla's ears burned for all she cared!

Anna rose from her seat, her mouth in a thin line of disapproval. She was throwing a temper tantrum which would do a two-year-old proud, but she was beyond caring any more. She was through running away, and the last couple of days had been filled with more spent emotion than she'd suffered through in years. She was just too tired to go on with the fight. Let David do his worst, but he would do it without her being present, she vowed silently, for she couldn't fight him anymore. If he dragged her to his room this minute, she thought wryly, she would let him have from her whatever he wanted . . . without a word of protest.

As if to show her what a liar she was, David's arm stole around her waist . . . and her first impulse was to run screaming from the room. It was as if her thoughts had taken on reality, and she bit her lip, her breath quickening as she strove for some measure of control. Carla was studying her face with an unusual amount of interest; and she seemed to be trying to stifle a great amount of hilarity at her expense, Anna thought.

Anna tried moving away from the warmth of David's body, but he pulled her back against his side without even pausing in the conversation he'd begun with Carla. She had worn wide-legged jersey slacks and a matching overblouse for practicality while working, as well as dressiness, and now she cursed herself for her choice. The thin material was next to useless, for she could feel the imprint of David's hip and thigh burning through her clothes. Not tucking the blouse in had been even more of a mistake, she thought, fighting for control of her breath as his hand slowly caressed the bare flesh above her waist.

"So, it's settled," David remarked with satisfaction. "I'll meet you in the foyer in an hour."

"What," Anna remarked nervously. "I . . . I'm afraid I wasn't listening. What's settled?"

Moving away from her, David looked with amusement at Anna's flushed face.

"That's what we didn't have a . . . chance . . . to discuss last night, Ann," he drawled, his eyes moving to her parted mouth, and a smile of memory flashing across his face. "We're going to take my cruiser out to San Diego Bay."

Seeing the protest forming on her lips, David didn't give her a chance to refuse, his lips firming and his eyes glinting a warning.

"It won't be a pleasure trip, Ann. Bring your camera, for I hope to get some shots of migrating whales. We won't be able to get too close, so bring a telephoto lens," he ordered, all traces of familiarity gone from his manner as he became every inch the boss.

Looking at Carla as David moved away, Anna just shrugged her shoulders at her friend's questioning look. That was the second time David had turned cold and abrupt in Carla's presence . . . and she could see that his sudden changes of mood intrigued her.

Walking back to their room to collect the equipment needed for their outing, Anna could see from the tense look on Carla's face that she was putting two and two together—and probably coming up with six! Well, she supposed she did owe Carla an explanation . . . for David's attitude left little doubt as to their intimacy. She certainly didn't want Carla thinking the wrong things about their relationship . . . though she by no means planned on telling her the whole truth!

Following Carla into their room, Anna turned and quietly closed the door, taking a deep breath and trying to formulate her thoughts. Facing Carla, who stood in the middle of the room, her hands on her hips in a belligerent stance, her attitude obviously demanding some kind of explanation, Anna's lips twisted wryly . . . and she prayed for guidance before beginning the first lie, which was rather incongruous under the circumstances!

"Anna, what gives?" Carla demanded, her face softening when she saw the anguish Anna was trying desperately to hide. "Honey, I know I joked about you and David getting it on together . . . but honestly that's all it was . . . joking. You're not the type to indulge in casual affairs and come out of it unhurt . . . and I wouldn't want to think it was my fault you . . ."

"Carla, nothing was your fault," Anna interrupted, appalled at Carla's reasoning. "This began before you ever met David."

"You mean yesterday on the beach?"

Anna ran a shaking hand through her hair, avoiding Carla's questioning glance. The explanations were running around in her head, but for the life of her she didn't know how to begin. Well, she'd just have to start at the beginning, she thought determinedly.

"Carla, it started with David five years ago," she explained bluntly, watching Carla's mouth open in surprise. "I'm sorry I didn't tell you the truth, evaded the truth rather . . . but I just didn't see any point in raking up the past."

"But, Anna," she exclaimed, her expression puzzled. "It seems to be too much of a coincidence, the two of you meeting here after all this time."

"There wasn't any coincidence to it," Anna remarked bitterly. "David did need a professional photographer for the convention, I'm not denying that . . . but the reason he hired me was more personal than he let on."

"You mean he deliberately planned to get you here? But why? I don't understand, Anna. After all, five years is a long time."

"Apparently not long enough, where Mr. Carmichael is concerned!"

"Anna, let's be realistic about this whole situation," Carla begged, upset by Anna's inference. "If you knew each other years ago, isn't it possible David was just trying to help your career? You know, sending a little business your way?"

"Oh, God! I wish that were true, Carla. How simple it would make the whole deplorable mess," she exclaimed, jumping up and walking over to the porthole, to stand staring sightlessly out at the horizon.

Slowly she began to speak, telling Carla of her meeting with David, but for some inexplicable reason not mentioning the fact they were married. Though she was deliberately fostering the belief in Carla's mind that they'd indulged in an affair, she was beyond caring. Far better for Carla to believe she'd been promiscuous, Anna thought, than to let her on to the truth. She made it sound to Carla as if they had made a mutual decision to part due to the pressure of both their careers.

There was no point in making David out to be the bad guy, Anna realized . . . for it would only make Carla prejudiced against him. They would have to meet him, both socially and otherwise, for the next few days, and it would be even more of an impossible position than it was already if Carla showed a grudge.

There was a tense silence in the room when she finished speaking. Her back was turned toward Carla, so she was unprepared when she felt her friend's hand on her shoulder.

"You love him, don't you?"

The quiet question took her entirely by surprise. She had tried to seem unconcerned, avoiding any reference to the hurt she'd suffered at his hands, but obviously hadn't succeeded.

Leaning her head tiredly against the wall, Anna closed her eyes tightly, fighting to force back the tears which were imminent. Her breath felt ragged, and she swallowed hard to obliterate the lump forming in her throat.

Oh, God! She didn't want Carla's pity, or anyone else's. It was hard enough trying to control herself as it was . . . any kindness would send her right over the edge. She had to convince Carla . . . had to show her that any love for David had died long ago. Straightening her shoulders, she turned to face her, determination in every line of her taut body.

"I . . . I d . . . don't," she began, but the words quivering uncertainly from her mouth trailed away into silence, the loving concern in Carla's face preventing her from uttering the lie.

David's harshness, his unrelenting siege to emotions she'd long bottled deep inside of her, had taken away any strength she'd ever possessed regarding him. Covering her face to hide the tears now coursing down her face, she groaned:

"Oh, God . . . yes! I love him, Carla . . . so much, so very much. Even if he doesn't want love from me, I can't stop myself from caring, and it's tearing me apart."

"Honey, if he doesn't love you," Carla soothed, leading Anna over to the bed and sitting beside her, "why would he go to all this trouble just to see you again?"

"Believe me, Carla," Anna muttered, wiping her cheeks with the back of her hand. "It wasn't love that motivated him."

"You know, Ann," Carla remarked musingly. "Many a great love began with lust. It's a rather primitive fact of

108

human nature. He may not love you . . . but you sure as hell disturb him if my old eyes haven't deceived me."

"Yes, and just where is that going to get me, Carla?" Anna exclaimed angrily. "I refuse to use my body to try and hold him . . . it didn't work before, after all."

"I'm not suggesting you should," Carla retorted, her voice sounding shocked at the suggestion. "You ought to know me better than that, Anna!"

Seeing the hurt in Carla's eyes, Anna felt ashamed of her outburst. Carla was being kind and only trying to help her . . . and she was taking out her pain and frustration on her.

"Oh, Carla," Anna moaned. "I'm sorry, I didn't mean that the way it sounded."

"I know, honey. You're upset, and I'm not making matters any better. What a stupid idiot I am, trying to put my nose where it doesn't belong," she exclaimed. "Just tell me to mind my own business!"

"Don't be silly," Anna exclaimed reassuringly. "If it were none of your business, then I wouldn't have tried to explain anything to you. I know I can trust you not to say anything to anyone."

"Mum's the word," Carla winked, rewarded by the slightly wavering smile Anna gave her. "Now, let's see about getting ready for this outing, okay? The sea air will probably do us both a lot of good . . . that is, if I don't get seasick."

Laughing with Carla, Anna quickly gathered the proper equipment for the trip, making sure they were packed securely in watertight cases just in case of any mishap. Snapping the last case closed, she walked to her suitcase, extracting a rather disreputable pair of jeans for the occasion. Carla had already changed into a nautical-looking outfit, navy blue slacks with a double-breasted jacket over a white turtleneck sweater. *Trust Carla to always wear the proper clothes,* Anna thought with a smile as she tugged on her jeans.

She wasn't making any efforts at dressing up to impress David, she thought as she tugged at the zipper. "Darn, either these things have shrunk or I've put on weight," she muttered, finally managing to get the zipper up.

"Well, you certainly haven't gained any weight," Carla laughed, surveying Anna's slim form with critical eyes. "I'd say rather the opposite is true."

"You're good for my ego."

"Not true," Carla rejoined. "It's just another way of telling you you're too skinny! Either that or you bought those things when you were about sixteen . . . and from the look of them that's entirely possible."

"Now I feel self-conscious, Carla," Anna remarked ruefully. "Maybe I'd better change. Do they really look that bad?"

"Hum . . . that's a matter of opinion. The way they show your figure isn't bad—on the contrary, I'd say."

"Now I know I'm going to change," Anna retorted, walking to the closet and rummaging through her hangers.

"Come on, I was only kidding. Anyway, there's not enough time left. We're supposed to be meeting David in ten minutes."

"It won't kill him to wait!"

"No, but really, those jeans are all right, Ann," Carla urged, her voice showing her exasperation. "Honestly, you're acting like some teenager getting ready for her first date!"

If there was anything that could have put a stop to her indecisiveness . . . that was it! Quickly grabbing a royal blue cashmere sweater, Anna pulled it over her head. Long-sleeved, it would probably be warm enough . . . but with its rather low V neck it would probably be safer to bring along her suede jacket, she thought, hurrying when she heard Carla utter an impatient sigh from the doorway.

Entering the foyer, they at first didn't see David, for his back was to them and he appeared to be deep in conversation with someone. Uttering a gasp, Anna recognized the other man. Carl! What in the world was he doing here?

"Carl, when did you get here?" Anna questioned almost feverishly. "I didn't know you planned on coming."

"Hello, darling," Carl remarked, turning and kissing Anna on the cheek. "I know you didn't, but I managed to get a few days off and thought I'd surprise you."

Anna looked rather nervously at David, expecting to see anger at Carl's kiss and use of endearment. Strangely enough he looked blandly amused, and Anna felt an irrational sense of chagrin stealing over her.

"Have you met each other?" Carla questioned, turning to smile at Carl.

"Yes, Mr. Carmichael introduced himself," Carl replied, smiling in turn at Carla. "I was having Anna paged, and he explained about your outing today. He's kindly asked me if I'd like to go along."

"The name's David, Carl . . . and I'm sure Ann would be pleased if you'd accompany us, wouldn't you?"

Anna wanted to wipe that expression of unholy amusement off his face . . . but this wasn't the time or place for a scene. Turning to Carl, she clutched his arm possessively, acting for all she was worth, and felt rewarded when she saw the frown cross David's face.

"Darling, what a wonderful surprise," she remarked, smiling up into Carl's face . . . her whole manner one of intimacy. "We'd love you to come along, wouldn't we, Carla?"

A strange expression crossed Carla's face momentarily, to be lost in the rather forced-looking smile she gave Anna.

"Of course, Carl," Carla remarked offhandedly. "We

111

were just leaving. I guess we can wait while you check in and take your baggage to your room," she concluded, looking inquiringly at David.

"No need, Carla," Carl remarked quietly, turning to smile at Anna. "Since this was a spur of the moment decision, I neglected to phone ahead for reservations . . . like a fool. When Mr. . . . David answered my page, I was busy hassling for apparently nonexistent accommodation. David has kindly offered me the use of his room."

"But—" Anna began doubtfully.

"That's quite all right, Ann," David drawled. "I have my boat docked nearby. I'll just move some of my things and sleep aboard her."

"David," Carl protested. "I didn't realize you'd have to go to so much trouble. Really, I'll just get a room at the hotel across the way."

Clasping Carl on the shoulder—as if they were long lost buddies, Anna thought waspishly—David smiled.

"There's no problem at all, Carl. I was planning to spend the next few nights aboard my cruiser anyway. My room, as luxurious as it is, has become rather claustrophobic. I've spent so many nights with the sea under me, it's getting rather difficult for me to sleep otherwise."

"Well, if you're sure, David," Carl remarked doubtfully.

"I'm sure," David smiled, turning to signal for a passing porter. "I'll have your luggage removed to your room. Is there anything you want from your cases? If so, we'll wait for you here while you follow the porter."

Carl looked down at himself, turning to Anna with an inquiring lift of his brows. "Am I adequately clothed for this kind of thing, Anna?"

"You're fine, Carl . . . don't fuss," Anna replied impatiently, surveying Carl's slacks and heavy cable-knit sweater.

Feeling ashamed of her curt remark, Anna smiled and hugged Carl's arm affectionately. Carla was quiet, looking

112

down at her feet, and as she glanced at David, she noted the angry pulsing in his jaw and his disapproving look. Carl's slight flush was now hidden by a smile, a smile she didn't deserve in the least. Poor Carl, why did he let her get away with this kind of behavior toward him. The sneer on David's face left her in no doubt as to what he would do if she ever dared talk to him that way!

Later David gave them a quick tour of his cruiser before they set out. It was much larger than the one he had when she'd known him before, Anna mused, impressed with its size and luxurious accommodations. There was a good-size galley, as well as a small sitting room fitted with low couches attached to the walls, with storage cabinets underneath. The cushions were black with gray swirls running through them, and the cabin was accented richly in wood which looked very much like teak . . . if she wasn't mistaken. Quaint-looking lanterns were fitted with brackets upon the wooden paneling and placed strategically for reading on either side of the couch.

David suggested they roam about at will while he made ready to cast off. Anna felt relieved when his overpowering presence was removed and glanced through the long rectangular windows, parting the curtains with her hand and taking a deep breath at the sight which met her eyes.

The sea was calm, only a gentle rocking motion beneath her feet attesting to her presence upon a boat, and the weather was perfect, the sky a brilliant slash of blue with the sun reflecting dancing prisms across the sea, turning the water to turquoise. A slight breeze scudded a few wispy streaks of clouds across the sky, and a mass of gulls, their cries raucous in the still air, caught her attention. Somehow they seemed to add a touch of reality to a scene nearly too perfect to be true, and a smile tugged at her mouth as they violently soared and dipped, fighting each other for supremacy. Opening the window, which was on a slide, Anna breathed deeply of the salty air, almost

113

feeling its moist scent while she listened to the gentle lapping of waves against the side of the boat. The combination of sights and sounds suddenly caused a feeling of intense exhilaration to course through her veins, and she almost felt angry when she was interrupted by Carl and Carla reentering the cabin.

"Anna, you've got to come and see this," Carla enthused, wicked lights dancing in her eyes.

"See what?"

"Just wait . . . you'll never believe it!"

"I think I'll join David up on deck," Carl remarked, avoiding Anna's eyes as he began climbing the stairs.

"What's the matter with Carl? He looked almost embarrassed," Anna asked, her eyes following Carl's quickly receding figure until he was out of sight.

"Oh! He's an old fuddy-duddy," Carla remarked, exasperation coating her voice with venom.

"Carla, I don't know why you've never liked Carl," Anna scolded. "He's a wonderful man and I wish you wouldn't goad him the way you do. I just don't understand you, you're always unfailingly polite to everyone else, even people you don't like. Can't you be a little kinder to Carl, at least for the next few days?"

"That would take more effort than I'm capable of," Carla muttered rebelliously.

"Carla . . ."

"Oh, all right," Carla smiled. "I'll do my best, but that man has a habit of rubbing me up the wrong way!"

A wry smile curved Anna's mouth. "I guess that's better than nothing. Now what was it you wanted to show me?"

Heavens! No wonder Carl looked embarrassed, Anna mused, trying to control her own fluttering pulse at the sight that met her eyes. She had just taken for granted that the couches in the main cabin served also as sleeping accommodations . . . she'd never expected anything like this! She had noticed another door beside the small but functional bathroom, but had just assumed it to be a storage area. In reality it was the most seductively designed bedroom she'd ever seen in her life! Leave it to David, she thought disparagingly, to have thought of something like this!

Instead of paneling the walls, he had left them bare, their surface painted a glistening white. That in itself would have been perfectly acceptable, if a trifle stark, but David hadn't left it there . . . not him! Instead there were wide swirls resembling tiger stripes painted diagonally across the far wall from floor to ceiling. Upon closer inspection Anna realized there were actually four separate strips curving a downward path, each approximately three inches wide, comprised of varying shades from black to gray, which made up the pattern of one of the massive stripes. The two feet of white wall between each slash of color seemed almost indecently pure against the boldness of the pattern . . . but that wasn't all that disturbed her calm!

What really caught the attention was a low, circular bed placed strategically in front of the wall. It was huge, and nearly filled the moderate size room. She couldn't help staring almost transfixed, and had to stop herself from reaching out and stroking the black velvet bedspread. Instead of completely covering the surface, the spread was turned back at the top, allowing a glimpse of white satin sheets, partially covered by two large bolster pillows, striped like the wall against which they rested.

The short wall to the left contained cleverly mirrored sliding doors. Anna had the insane desire to yell stop when Carla slid one open. God only knew, she thought hysterically, what they'd find! She was glad she hadn't embarrassed herself by crying out, for all the glass doors hid was a walk-through wardrobe, one end of which contained fitted drawers and shelves containing linen. Even so she couldn't help feeling relieved when Carla pulled the door shut, and she licked her suddenly dry lips nervously.

That's all she'd need, for David to walk in and find them nosing around his personal possessions!

"Come on, Carla," she muttered. "Let's get out of here."

"What do you think, Anna," Carla breathed, turning and winking at her. "Don't you think it's . . . scrumptious?"

"Decadent is more like it."

"Hmmm," Carla breathed, a mocking smile curving her lips. "That too."

"Just a minute, Anna. Let's just flick the light switch. I want to see what it looks like."

"Carla, I just don't feel right invading David's privacy like this. Come on. . . ."

The only light had come from the open door behind them, the two portholes on the far wall covered at the moment. As Carla suited action to words, the room was subtly bathed in a soft, muted glow which cast shadows across the bed, its prisms gleaming against the rich wood flooring. The illumination came from a large white sphere hanging directly over the bed.

"Wow? It certainly makes the room look inviting, especially when the light sways and casts those rippling shadows."

"About as inviting as a web to a fly," Anna quipped, the smile she was trying to give Carla not quite succeeding.

Carla tilted her head at Anna's stilted tone of voice, looking at her with a quizzical gleam. "You may be right, honey. He sure didn't design this room with the idea of reading in bed!"

Anna felt herself flush, and hated herself for her lack of control. She was acting like a gauche teenager, for goodness sake! Setting her face she replied cooly, "No, I'm sure he didn't!"

"Mmmm," Carla sighed, looking suggestively at Anna

116

out of the corner of her eyes. "I wonder what it'd be like to . . ."

To avoid hearing the last of Carla's remark Anna pivoted sharply, unable to prevent uttering a choked cry as she stormed from the bedroom. She practically ran across the wood flooring of the main cabin, and was ascending the stairs when she heard Carla's laughter, which fanned the final embers of her chagrined anger.

Emerging into the sunlight, Anna walked over to her equipment. The brisk ocean breeze was cool against her heated cheeks, and as she looked back at the quickly receding shoreline, she felt slightly more composed. It was a perfect day to be out on the sea, and the thought of possibly catching a glimpse of the migrating whales was certainly an exciting one.

It was foolish not to take the opportunities offered because of irrational anger at David. She was beginning to live too much on her emotions because of him, and it was time she began acting more rationally. As she mentally scolded herself, she found herself walking the circumference of the ship, holding tightly to the rails as the deck rocked beneath her feet. She couldn't help wondering how Carl was taking the vessel's pitching and rolling, for the farther out they got, the higher the waves became. She hoped he didn't spend the entire trip seasick . . . she wouldn't want the outing spoiled for him. Where was he anyway?

Carla was still down below, and knowing their antipathy for each other, she was certain Carl would spend as little time alone with Carla as he could get away with. . . . Since he wasn't on deck, he must be helping steer a course with David. Who was she kidding, she thought wryly, turning her feet resolutely toward the wheelhouse. She was dying for any excuse to see the rest of the boat, especially the navigation equipment. With a cruiser of this size, with the obviously few restrictions made as to luxury, it must have the very latest and best equipment possible. As long as Carl was with David, she felt justified in seeking him out. At least David wouldn't think her curiosity was eagerness to be alone with him!

Her steps were eager as she climbed lithely upward, and entering the small confined space surrounded entirely in glass, she felt glad she'd taken the trouble. The view from this height was tremendous, and she stared out at the teaming waves in awe, completely ignoring the presence of the two men. The horizon was lovely, brilliantly blue sky seeming to merge with the blue-green of the sea until it was difficult to decide where one stopped and the other began.

"Anna, why didn't you let us know you were here?" Carl exclaimed, turning his head to question David and seeing her silently standing behind them. The noise of the engines had muffled the sound of her footsteps, and when she saw the sardonic expression on David's face . . . she was sorry she hadn't announced herself before being discovered. David's attitude seemed to imply she'd been trying to spy on their male conversation, and she flushed angrily at his silent criticism.

"I haven't been here long," she smiled sweetly up at Carl before turning to David with a haughty expression. "I was just admiring the view from up here—it's beautiful."

David turned to make a slight adjustment to one of the many dials in front of him, taking his time before answering.

"Don't be taken in, Ann," he muttered. "Many things are beautiful, but that doesn't make them any less deadly. The sea, like a woman, can be unpredictable, and a man can become so ensnared that he loses everything at her hands."

Drawing in her breath to make an acid rejoinder, Anna hesitated, and the moment was lost. There was something in the tautness of David's shoulders which warned her

118

against trying to match wits with him at this particular moment . . . or maybe it was just cowardice, coupled with a strange reluctance to spoil the beauty of the day by exchanging any more barbed remarks.

Walking forward to get a better view of the compass, Anna was surprised when David, sensing her interest, began explaining the uses of the equipment. It was amazingly complex, and when she remarked upon this, he agreed. The reason, she found, was that the cruiser had been outfitted for oceanographical studies and not solely for pleasure. As if to emphasize that point, David showed her the sonar equipment he'd had installed to enable him to listen to the songs of the whales as well as to follow them. Also, David explained, the sonar was useful in placing, and thus avoiding, hidden obstacles.

Anna had been vaguely aware of Carl's departure, for he'd politely made his good-bye's before leaving them, but she'd been so engrossed in the equipment and David's explanations, she hadn't paid much attention other than a casual wave of her hand. But suddenly she was aware of the closeness of David's body, as well as the warmth which emanated from him, and realized that she hadn't noticed that his arm had circled her waist some time during the discussion.

"I think I'll join the others, David," she muttered, attempting to turn away from his arm casually, as if she were unaffected by his hold on her.

"Not yet," he murmured, tightening his arm and pulling her closer.

His mouth moved on hers with devastating warmth, parting her lips effortlessly as he fully plundered the sweetness within. Anna felt herself relax against him, her body seeming to melt into his. Just as hot flames of desire shuddered through her defenseless body, David ended the kiss, his hand gently brushing a stray wisp of curl from

119

her cheek. As she looked at him in bewildered surprise, she noted a brooding sadness in his expression.

"David, I . . ."

"Hush, don't explain the moment Ann," he whispered, the huskiness of his voice attesting to the fact that he hadn't been entirely unmoved by passion. "I hear Carla calling . . . hadn't you better see what she wants?"

"Yes . . . of course, David," she replied, feeling a chill which had nothing to do with the elements shiver across her body as she left him.

CHAPTER SEVEN

She hurried down onto the main deck in search of Carla, unable to understand or dispel the lingering sadness she felt. When she had turned for a last glance at David, he had returned her look, but she had noticed with dismay that his habitually cold mask was once more in place, as if he meant her to know his gentleness had been nothing more than a momentary lapse. Only . . . he'd looked so lonely for that moment before he had once again donned his armor. Strangely enough, whether she had imagined it or not, her impression had caused emotion to unfurl painfully inside of her . . . and she couldn't tell if what she felt was pity for herself . . . or David.

They reached their destination all too soon for Anna, although judging by the relief on Carl's face, he didn't share her opinion. While she stood in solitary enjoyment against the rails, Carl had been sitting in a deck chair behind her, the fresh breezes helping to dispel at least some of his queasiness.

As she turned to smile at him, her mouth opened in surprise to see Carla, her own chair pulled close to Carl's, holding a desultory conversation with him. Either Carla had just gotten bored by herself or she really was making some attempt at being polite, Anna thought, turning around once more to hide her smile.

The engines were throttling down now as David turned around the headland, the boat gliding smoothly into the San Diego Bay. Shading her eyes, she looked toward the shore, but the glare of the sun prevented her from seeing clearly. The only impression she got was of rocky green knolls coupled with indistinct signs of civilization. The area was highly populated, but from this distance she was unable to make anything out in detail.

Eventually they weighed anchor, the throbbing engines strangely silent as the boat rocked gently upon the waves. Anna was glad the sea was now calm. If they were able to spot the migrating whales, it would make her job that much easier, and she felt a swell of excitement at the possibility of getting some really good photographs. Her equipment was checked and double-checked, and now she waited with anticipation, talking quietly to Carl.

As she'd approached them, Carla had given Anna a strangely sheepish look before hurrying away to prepare lunch. Anna had offered to help her, but Carla had vetoed the suggestion, saying it would be better if she were on deck in case the whales were spotted. Carla was right . . . but her attitude was rather puzzling. It had seemed as if Carla were avoiding her company for one reason or another. Really, she thought, smiling as she listened to Carl extolling the virtues of dry land. She had become so emotionally distraught over the last few days that she was even ready to imagine slights where none existed! Certainly Carl seemed his usual self, even if he did look a little green around the gills, she thought with amusement.

"What's so funny?" David asked.

Anna jumped, unaware of his approach until he spoke from just behind her.

"Must you always sneak up on people like that?" Anna

122

exclaimed, glaring at him when he walked around her to take the seat next to Carl.

"What's the matter, Ann," he questioned hatefully. "Guilty conscience?"

At that moment Carla approached laden with a tray piled high with sandwiches, thick earthenware mugs giving off the delectable aroma of coffee. Carl jumped up to take the tray from Carla, murmuring his appreciation before setting the lunch down on an adjacent table. Reaching for a sandwich, Anna automatically smiled at Carla, noting the slight flush on her face.

David had briefly gone below, returning moments later with two more deck chairs. As they sat there eating, the sun warming them, Anna felt an unexpected sense of well-being. If anyone had told her yesterday that she'd feel comfortable in David's presence, she would have laughed herself silly. *Still*, she thought wonderingly . . . *it's true*. Finished with her sandwich, she held her coffee between her hands, enjoying the warmth penetrating her skin and enjoying also the gentle raillery going on between Carl and David. They were arguing over the outcome of the last Raiders game, heads bent over a drawing Carl had made on his napkin.

Strange, she mused. David and Carl were totally different personalities, and she would never have expected them to get on together. Yet here they were, laughing and talking as if they were old friends. She couldn't help wondering what David's game was. He had made no attempt to be other than charming to her friends, winning them over apparently without effort.

Even she had no complaints on that score, she thought ruefully, for just then David looked up, meeting her eyes and smiling gently. She nearly choked on her coffee, for there had been only warmth and sweetness in his expression, and none of the coldness she'd come to expect from him.

Pain welled deeply, attacking her with sudden devastation. At that moment she knew, finally and irrevocably, that she loved David with an intensity which frightened her. Staring down into her cup to hide her expression, Anna fought the tears of self-pity welling in her eyes. With a strength she never knew she possessed she fought them back, unwilling to make more of a fool of herself than she was already.

She was absolutely crazy, she thought hysterically. How could she have let him weave his spell around her again when he'd treated her so cruelly in the past? Anna faced the question with honesty. The truth was painful, but it had to be faced, she thought with resignation. No matter how she'd attempted to deny the memories, to shut him out of her mind, she'd never been able to obliterate his image from her heart.

David wanted her, and God help her . . . she was glad! How terrible it would have been, how infinitely worse, if she had met him again and been treated impersonally, as if she'd had little or no effect on his life. That would have been an unbearable stripping away of her pride, as well as a mockery of the happiness she'd known with him so briefly.

Where did she go from here, she wondered. David had left her in no doubt as to his plans for her . . . so how in the world would she handle the situation when he felt the time was right to exert his total mastery over her? There wasn't a doubt in her mind that he would succeed, for she had no defense against the love she felt for him. To fight David would be to fight herself, and with a sigh she knew there was very little fight left in her. Raising brooding eyes to his, she felt her pulse quicken and an intense longing to be in his arms tore through her.

The silent communication between them was interrupted by an excited shout from Carla, who was just stepping onto the deck after returning the tray to the galley. Following her pointing finger, Anna jumped up, nearly running toward her camera in her eagerness. There they were, far off in the distance . . . a vast herd of humpbacked whales surfacing majestically. While David handed around binoculars, Anna zoomed them in with her telephoto lens . . . gasping at their size and splendor, huge bodies glistening as the sun reflected rippling slivers of light upon their backs.

They appeared to be moving leisurely, occasionally slapping their tails on the water and sending forth spumes of spray. Anna was amazed at how close they sounded, although she realized from her studies that their tails slapping the water could be heard for miles. Sometimes they seemed to leap out of the water, only to plunge back in head first, their tails standing straight on end before they disappeared beneath the surface. This procedure, David explained, was called breaching. No one knew why they did it, but since both sexes and all age groups performed this maneuver often on their migration, quite possibly, he theorized, it was a form of play.

Anna felt her hands shaking with eager excitement. These shots needed all the technical skill she could give them if they were to turn out the way she wished. She could hear the low rumble of Carl's voice in the background mingling with Carla's excited questions. David was answering to the best of his not inconsiderable ability, and she was relieved at not being included in the conversation. David seemed to understand her need for solitude and was urging Carla and Carl farther away; she paused in her work long enough to give him a grateful smile.

With warmth flooding through her at that brief moment of shared understanding, Anna once again turned her thoughts inward. She knew that optically any extensive view of the ocean demands precision of detail, for textures must be retained in the final image. This being especially true in the sheen of sunlight on wave crests, which both factually and emotionally is very sharp and incisive, she quickly adjusted her camera accordingly, using a lower filter than she had at first decided upon.

After an hour, she felt limp when at last the herd disappeared from sight. Once more packing away her equipment, she couldn't help feeling apprehensive. What if they didn't turn out? There wouldn't be another opportunity, for they'd be leaving for home the day after tomorrow. It was so important that she catch the right emotive quality in the pictures, something that would appeal to the most hardened of skeptics . . . and she knew that if these photos turned out, she would have accomplished just that!

The whales had been in a playful mood, surfacing regularly and performing graceful surface maneuvers in the waves. She had managed to get several shots of them breaching, their huge bodies nearly standing completely on end.

These shots alone would be spectacular, but she had also gotten pictures of them flippering, raising their flippers high out of the water from a side position. Their underbellies had gleamed white before they slapped the water with their fins, and she knew the contrast against the almost unearthly blue of the ocean would be gorgeous.

Anna smiled as she remembered hearing the low murmur of David's voice in the distance as he explained this particular phenomenon. He had given several suppositions as to the reason the whales used their fins in this manner.

Anna's face softened as she thought of the emotive quality in David's voice as he talked of the creatures' intelligence and also, despite their size, their gentleness. Why this side of David, a side showing both sensitivity and caring, should pull at her emotions so evocatively was obvious when coupled with her new insights into her own feelings.

David was the kind of man, she thought, to care deeply about the effect man has upon the future environment, and unlike others, was trying to do something about it.

No matter how he had treated her in the past, she couldn't shake the belief that basically David was a caring man, revering life in its entirety. Who knew, she thought, clenching her fists against her sides and staring blindly oceanward . . . maybe he blamed her for the accident which had taken their baby's life! There was so much unexplained between them, so much that needed to be said.

Then again maybe she was just grasping at straws, wanting desperately to justify her continuing love for him. But then did love ever need justifying? she wondered. Wasn't it just a reality, as much a reality as life itself, and like life . . . tenacious in its ability to survive? If only that tiny promise of life she had carried within her had been as tenacious, she mourned.

Strangely she had never felt her loss as acutely as she did at that moment. She had thought all her grief behind her in the shadowy past, but now with a wrenching agony she realized the pain was as real to her at this moment as it had been the day she lay, a silent and white-faced girl in an impersonal hospital bed, staring mutely at the ceiling after being told that her child no longer existed for her.

With a sickening plunge into the present she felt David's hands on her shoulders, his touch caressingly firm as he massaged away her tenseness. With a sigh she leaned against the comforting solidarity of his body, needing him as much now as she had that day so long ago. She felt his arms come around her, crossing over her breasts as his chin came down to rest upon the top of her head. Suddenly she felt revitalized, as if being held in his arms was evoking a healing influence, cleansing away much of the pain and disillusionment of the past.

The warmth of his body began having its usual effect upon her, and she pulled away from the torment of his touch self-consciously. Glancing surreptitiously over his shoulder, to her immense relief she noted that Carl and Carla were no longer standing by the bow.

"Where are the others?"

"What the hell difference does it make?" David replied, reaching out once more and pulling her against his hard frame. At Anna's reproachful stare he relented, smoothing her hair from the side of her flushed face with a gentle hand.

"Oh, all right," he muttered against her forehead as his mouth moved caressingly against her skin. "I told them we wanted to be alone for a few moments."

"But Carl . . ." she began, only to have his hand on her chin stop her words as he jerked her head back violently.

"Carl's not for you, blue eyes," he muttered warningly, his eyes shooting green sparks as they glinted at her against the mahogany tan of his face. "You belong to me, and I intend to have you, Carl or no Carl!"

With a groan David bent his head and caressed the tautness of her mouth, his own firm and warm, teasing her flesh with his teeth and tongue until hers softened and opened to his moist penetration. Returning his kiss fully, Anna slipped her hands around his back, caressing the rippling muscles eagerly as desire rose in her. With a muttered curse David tore his mouth from hers, enfolding her even more tightly in his embrace and leaving her in no doubt as to the extent of his arousal as he thrust his hardened thighs against her.

"I can't take much more of this, Ann," he gasped, his mouth moving slowly over the pulsating vein at the side of her neck.

"David, please let me explain about Carl," she begged, as soon as her erratic pulses slowed.

"You forget, I had you investigated, Ann," he replied harshly, his body stiff as he turned away from her to clutch at the rails beside them.

Anna froze at his words. She had forgotten the full extent of David's ruthlessness until his words reminded her. Mouth dry, she asked, "Just what did you determine from these . . . investigations?"

At the insolent mockery in her voice David spun around, his eyes burning hotly down at her. His arms moved on either side of his body as he leaned, apparently at his ease, against the rail . . . but Anna realized how erroneous that impression was just by glancing at his hands, which were gripping the rail so tightly, the knuckles showed white.

"All right, Ann. Since you've asked, I'll tell you. I know how many evenings you've spent with Carl, where you've gone, and also where you've ended up," he exclaimed, anger and frustration apparent in his voice.

"What do you mean, where we've ended up?" Anna questioned, her own anger rising at the implications in his voice.

"Does it matter whose apartment it was, Ann?" David asked tiredly, his anger seeming to leave his body as abruptly as it had entered it. "Look, I'm not blaming you for anything."

"It sounds very much like it, David," she retorted, staring up at him defiantly.

Straightening, David pulled her resisting body close, his hand then moving to cup her cheek, one finger moving slowly to outline the curve of her mouth. At his touch she had to fight herself not to gasp aloud, her heart beginning to pound with a different emotion than anger.

"Ann," he whispered. "Can you imagine how I felt when I read those reports? God, I went through agony, remembering the way you looked in my bed and knowing he was in your apartment . . . your bed. Meeting Carl, I was at first surprised by your choice of a lover until I began talking to him. To my surprise I found myself liking

129

him, yet at the same time wanting to punch his face in. Can you imagine that?"

In a voice faint with shock Anna mumbled, "Yes, David. I don't have any difficulty at all imagining it."

Gazing at David incredulously, she could hardly believe the depths of his arrogance. Even though she loved him, she couldn't let him think he could just walk back into her life and take over. He believed Carl had been her lover, did he? *Well,* she thought viciously . . . *let him!* He obviously wouldn't believe any protestations of hers to the contrary, so why should she bother trying to explain their relationship?

"If you felt that way, David," she questioned, tilting her chin defiantly, "then what took you so long to put a stop to it?"

To her surprise David avoided her eyes, lowering his to study the deck and raking a hand through the thickness of his hair before replying. "I've only just returned to this country, that's why. Believe me, I would have preferred continuing my work in France, where I was lucky enough to be chosen for some of the Cousteau expeditions, but this became impossible unless I was willing to forego my other business interests."

"That still doesn't answer my question, David."

Raising tormented eyes to hers, David's mouth firmed angrily. "You want your pound of flesh, don't you Ann? All right, I'll tell you—and then you can have a good laugh at my expense, hmmm?"

Anna stepped backward, resisting the childish impulse to cover her ears with her hands. The look on David's face, one of self-contempt mingled with hatred, was causing an insane desire in her to flee from his cruelty.

"Don't run away," he mocked. "You wanted the truth, and you're going to get it. While in France or away for months at a time at sea I was able to get on with my life. Eventually, though, I had to return to San Francisco . . . it

130

is my home after all. I was confident that I'd long ago gotten you out of my system, so you can imagine the self-disgust I felt when everything I saw reminded me of you, and everywhere I went your ghost followed me. The only solution was for me to leave town again, but I was damned if I would. Instead I hired the detective to trace you . . . you already know the rest."

All those months of torment when she'd searched for his face in the crowds, totally without pride in her longing for him . . . until she drove her own misery inward, forcing herself to survive when all she had wanted was to die. All those months of self-inflicted torture, and now to find that he'd been thousands of miles away from her!

"Did you hear what I said, Ann?" David questioned impatiently.

"I'm sorry, David," she apologized absently, giving a slight gasp when his hands tightened relentlessly on her arms.

As he heard her gasp and noticed the pained expression crossing her face, David relented slightly, easing his ruthless hold on her, but making no other concessions . . . such as apologizing for causing her pain, she thought with resentment.

"I'm asking you to let Carl down easily," David explained arrogantly. He's a nice guy, and he's obviously crazy about you . . . but I want him out of the picture."

"What happens then, David," she retorted mockingly. "You got me here for one purpose—to prove to yourself that I mean little or nothing to you. What happens after you've exorcised my ghost to your satisfaction? Do you walk out on me again?"

"Damn you, Ann. I . . ." David began furiously, only to be interrupted by a shout from Carla.

Anna felt relief flooding through her at the timely interruption. She had flayed David with the bitterness of her thoughts, but, God help her, she wasn't ready to hear his

131

answer. She was at the end of her endurance where he was concerned, and though she knew it didn't do any good to stick her head in the sand, at least she could delay the inevitable disillusionment.

She couldn't help admiring the way David quickly controlled his anger. The calm, friendly appearance he was showing to Carla was completely contrary to what he was feeling, and the angry muscle jumping in his cheek only corroborated her suppositions.

"Carl wants to know if there's a possibility of eating dinner on dry land," Carla laughed, her eyes twinkling at David.

"I think that can be arranged," he smiled. "Tell him I'd already made reservations at the Hotel del Coronado. It's a Victorian resort, and I thought you girls would enjoy seeing the place where the first colored electric lights were strung on a Christmas tree," he laughed, as if offering a special treat to children, Anna thought resentfully.

"That would be wonderful, David," Carla responded, oblivious to Anna's anger. "To tell you the truth I don't think Carl would care where it was as long as it didn't move about."

"You know, if Carl's off-color, it might be a good idea if I rented rooms for all of us," he suggested blandly, smiling at the indignant expression on Anna's face.

"I'll ask him," Carla responded, moving across the deck with alacrity.

"Just what do you have in mind, David?" Anna hissed, longing to wipe the mocking smile off his face.

"You know what I have in mind, honey," he grinned unrepentantly. "Don't worry, I can wait until there's no audience, though I don't really give a damn if they know you're in my bed."

Before she could respond to his outrageous remark, the other two returned. Her heart sank as Carl enthusiastically agreed to David's suggestion. She felt trapped by a situation which was quickly getting out of control, and as she turned to argue their decision, she was stopped by the look on Carl's face.

Poor Carl, his seasickness was apparently worse than she'd realized, and his skin had a gray cast which was indicative of his suffering. Never having suffered from seasickness herself, . . . still she could sympathize with his discomfort and understand his eagerness to get off the boat.

As David left to start the engine, she and Carla helped Carl over to a deck chair.

"Sorry about this, Anna," Carl mumbled, sitting back with a sigh. "I didn't mean to spoil everyone's outing."

"You haven't spoiled anything, you nit," Carla retorted, much to Anna's surprise. "You've been fighting it off, not saying a word, even though I could see you were feeling worse as time went on. You should have said something sooner, but no . . . you prefer to suffer in silence. That's just like a man."

"Yes, and don't you forget it!" Carl exclaimed, his eyes on Carla's startled face.

"F . . . forget what?" Carla stuttered, trying to regain her composure.

"That I am a man," Carl whispered meaningly.

Carla's face flamed with color, and with a guilty glance at Anna she mumbled an excuse to go below.

"Well, well . . . what was all that about?" Anna teased, looking at Carl with new respect.

"I've just realized something, Anna," he remarked seriously. "Every time I've met Carla, she's irritated me by making snide remarks, and for some reason I couldn't understand, I've always let her get to me. Do you know what I mean?"

"Of course I do. In fact, I've never known Carla to behave badly to anyone but you, Carl. That's something I've never understood . . . but I think I'm beginning to."

Carl laughed, and with a smile on her face Anna relaxed in the chair next to him.

"Yes, and now I know why she's always been able to get a rise out of me. I may be slightly paunchy and middle-aged, but I think the girl fancies me."

"But how in the world did you guess, Carl," she questioned. "She's been very adept at hiding her feelings."

"Remember earlier when we were checking out that seduction pit David calls a bedroom?" At his question Anna's lips momentarily tightened in remembered jealousy, but forcing herself to assume a nonchalance she was far from feeling, she nodded.

"Well," Carl smiled reminiscingly. "We walked inside the room, just staring around in surprised awe more or less, and I turned to make some damned innocuous remark to her—you know my usual kind of thing," he said wryly. "Anyway, when I looked at her standing in front of that sexy bed, all I wanted to do at that moment was to jump on her bones."

"Carl," Anna squealed, delighted laughter pouring from her mouth. "I never knew you had it in you!"

"Neither did I," he laughed, shaking his head ruefully. "I'm not saying I'm a saint, Anna . . . far from it. A man doesn't get to be my age without having women, but I've always paid for what I wanted," he remarked honestly. "I've steered clear of emotional involvements other than the one I have with you, Anna. I think that's why we've lasted so long, because I knew you didn't want me as anything other than a friend. I would have married you to keep that friendship, because through you I've come to realize how lonely I really am."

"But how did you realize something like that because of me?"

"Do you want the truth, Anna?"

"Yes," she whispered.

"That night we were dining out about a year ago, when

you were coming down with the flu? Do you remember?"

Anna thought back, and suddenly she remembered the incident Carl was referring to. He'd brought her home early and before he left, had insisted she get into bed. After dosing her with aspirin—for by that time she was slightly feverish—he had left. What did that have to do with anything, she wondered.

"I was nervous about leaving you alone, so I closed your bedroom door so I wouldn't disturb you and returned to the living room. Around two o'clock I heard you cry out and went to check on you. You were having a nightmare, Anna. I heard you crying and . . ." Carl stopped speaking, looking at her with pitying eyes, emotion choking his voice as he noticed the white-faced misery in her expression. "Darling, I'm sorry. I should have kept my mouth shut."

"Please, Carl," she murmured. "I want you to tell me everything."

With a resigned nod of his head in her direction, he continued. "I heard you crying and moaning, 'my baby, oh please God, not my baby,' and I walked over to the bed, debating upon whether or not I should wake you up. I walked to the side of the bed and grasped your hand. You immediately stopped crying, clutching at my hand as if you'd never let me go. I sat beside you, and you murmured, 'I love you' . . . I held your hand until you were sleeping peacefully. Your fever was down by then, so I gathered together my things and left for home. That night as I lay in bed, I couldn't sleep. I kept thinking what a fool he was, that man you'd loved so deeply . . . that is, if he'd left you. From that moment on I longed to have someone love me that much, when just the touch of my hand could give them peace."

By the time he had finished, Anna was too overcome to speak. She looked at Carl with eyes eloquent with gratitude. Placing her hand over his, she whispered, "Carla doesn't know how lucky she is, my wonderful Carl."

"Doesn't this look cozy," David murmured from just behind them. "In case anyone cares, we've just docked."

She and Carl just looked at each other in consternation as David's quickly furious strides took him out of sight. They hadn't even noticed the stoppage of the engines.

David had told her he wanted Carl out of her life, and it was obvious he'd misinterpreted what he had just seen. With a sinking feeling in the pit of her stomach, she couldn't help wondering if he had also heard her whispered words.

"That man from your past . . . it was David, wasn't it, Anna?"

Looking into Carl's sympathetic face, Anna just mutely nodded, and Carl's hand reached out to cover her own.

Later, dining in the Coronado's restaurant, Anna let the conversation flow around her, not caring about the concerned looks she was getting from Carl. She had to come to terms with what he had told her, and it wouldn't be easy.

She couldn't help feeling envious of the way Carl was looking at Carla, or the happy flush on her face. Oh, they were being subtle, and she was sure that David couldn't sense anything different in their relationship . . . but it was obvious to her. Carla was no longer snipping at Carl, and there was a radiance lighting her friend's face that hadn't been there before.

Carl was looking better, too, and she was glad they'd been able to rent rooms for the night, even though David's brooding silence was beginning to affect her nerves. Just to be on the safe side she had insisted upon Carla sharing her room, and she hadn't needed to look at David to sense his anger.

Raising her eyes, she was startled to discover David staring at her, his green eyes narrowed in speculation. As the expression on his face darkened, she caught her breath, her face mirroring her rejection of the magnetic attraction pulling darkly between them. It was obvious what he wanted at that moment, but after Carl's revelations earlier she felt too torn apart with remembered pain to willingly bring any more upon herself.

To hear someone else mention the grief she'd hidden from everyone somehow made it even more vivid. She had gotten hurt before, loving David, and though she still loved him, was she really willing to risk having her life torn apart on his whim? She needed time to think without being influenced by his presence, for when he was near, she was unable to think at all, only feel!

Ever since he'd come back into her life, he had acted like a catalyst, breaking the fragile threads of her present existence and forcibly thrusting her into an emotionalism she'd thought herself no longer capable of. Things would never be the same, even if he walked out of here now and she never saw him again.

For the first time in years the shell of aloofness she had smothered herself in was gone, and strangely enough she didn't mourn its passing, for once again she felt fully alive, she realized wonderingly.

"Will you two excuse us? There are some things I'd like to discuss with Ann before bed," David remarked, rising to his feet. Startled out of her pensive reveries, Anna looked up at him as he towered over her.

"Is this necessary, David?" she asked, her voice quavering despite her attempt to steady it."

"Extremely necessary," he retorted, his words coldly precise. "We can talk while we take a walk along the beach."

Relief flooding through her at his mention of the beach, Anna got up to accompany him. They hadn't even turned away before Carl and Carla were once more sitting with their heads together after murmuring a polite good-night.

David strode out of the restaurant, pulling her by the hand and forcing her into a near-run to keep up with him.

"Where are we going," she gasped, trying to pull away from his grasp. "This isn't the way to the beach."

David didn't say a word, just sent her a disgusted glance from under darkening brows before pushing her rudely into the elevator.

"That's obvious," he remarked contemptuously, leaning his body indolently against the wall of the elevator as it began to move upward.

"I refuse to go to your room, David," she warned, meeting the contempt in his gaze unflinchingly.

"Would you prefer we discussed things in front of your friends?"

Anna bit her lip, holding back her angry words with an immense effort. David meant what he said, she realized. He wouldn't be above dragging everything out in front of Carl and Carla if she didn't concede to his wishes. Being alone with him was dangerous, especially in her weakened frame of mind, but it was true they had to talk, and she knew with a certainty that for her there could be no more running away.

CHAPTER EIGHT

Anna's first glimpse of David's room undermined her resolution to remain cool. Unlike other hotel rooms, this one had the warmth of another century. The furniture was dark and cumbersome, as were most Victorian period pieces, but still managed to retain a charm and warmth of another era, as if time had stood still. She almost embarrassed herself by gasping at her first glimpse of the massive bed which held pride of place in the center of the room, skirting it nervously in favor of a curved brocaded loveseat situated in front of the fireplace along the far wall.

As she stood uncertainly in front of the small couch, Anna felt her nerves stretching to breaking point. Turning, she found that in her haste she'd missed the fact that David had followed her. Involuntarily she stepped back, unable to bear his closeness.

"If I were in your shoes, I think I'd back up, too," he hissed, his body taut with rage too long suppressed. "After hearing 'my wonderful Carl' and breaking up the tender love scene, I wanted nothing more than to wring your neck!"

"Damn you, David. Why do you always think the worst," she raged, not fearing his anger and in a way almost welcoming the release for her emotions. "Carl is my friend, and he'd just told me something pretty wonderful, considering the way I've taken advantage of him over the years. I refuse to let you dictate my relationships, David. Carl was there when I needed him, you weren't. The way things stand, you've forfeited any rights in my life . . . and I'm damned if I'll just calmly stand back and let you walk all over me."

Anna was breathing quickly by the time she finished her tirade, but instead of feeling upset she felt almost exhilarated. David hadn't moved, but just remained as still as a graven image, and as she looked at him, she felt a further quickening of her pulses.

His black slacks moulded the muscled hardness of his thighs as he stood with his feet slightly apart, hands on his hips. His white shirt clung to his body, the position of his arms causing the material to stretch tautly over his chest, the first two buttons undone to show the beginning of the mat of dark hair which she knew traveled down below his beltline in a silken tangle. She had loved running her hands from his chest down over the muscled flatness of his stomach, all the while reveling in the power she had over his body.

Anna bit her lip at the sensuousness of the memory, beginning to turn away from him, her body stiff with repressed longing.

"All right, Ann," he muttered, his voice hoarse with emotion. "Maybe I did misconstrue the situation with Carl, but when I saw the way you were looking at him, the tenderness in your face, what the hell was I supposed to think?"

"You were wrong, but that's beside the point. Let me ask you a question, David. If I were in love with Carl," she said, looking up at him quietly, "would you let me go?"

For a moment he just stood still, his eyes devouring her tense form. A strange expression crossed his face fleetingly, then was gone. Even before he began shaking his head negatively, Anna knew the answer to her question, for his hands reached out and pulled her unresisting body against his, and as she was pressed close, she felt his body trembling revealingly.

Leaning against him, her own response was making her too weak to resist the potent warmth of his body . . . the clean male smell of him mingling in her nostrils. She couldn't fight herself any longer. There was no reason to think things out any more, for she realized that no matter what conclusions she came to about the future, they wouldn't affect the general outcome.

Her need to belong to David for however brief a time far outweighed any other considerations. If there was to be pain eventually, she would have to risk it, for she really had no other choice.

No one is able to cushion themselves from the hurts life can inflict. She knew that better than most, she thought wryly. With a new wisdom she realized that even if it were possible, she wouldn't want to. Each hurt in life was a part of living, making one stronger or destroying a person completely.

She had made it through nearly intolerable pain and loneliness before, and if she had to . . . she would again. With a spurt of optimism she snuggled closer in David's arms, for whatever happened, she knew now that she was one of life's survivors.

Tentatively her arms went around his waist until her palms lay against his back, and she reveled in the feel of his rippling muscles tensing against her hands. Looking up, she met his eyes which stared somberly down at her, as if he sensed the immensity of the decision she had to make. Slowly his lips met hers in a kiss evocative of mutual hunger and need.

David eventually broke the kiss, and she shuddered at the consuming fire in his gaze, closing her eyes in reaction to his sensual demand. His mouth moved in softly tormenting butterfly kisses across her eyes, her cheeks, and down her neck, where they finally lingered, plundering the throbbing pulse they found there.

The sensations pulsing through Anna were a pleasure half mingled with pain, and she was barely aware of David carrying her across the room to lay her tenderly upon the bed. Hands on either side of her head, he leaned over her, the sweetness of his breath mingling with hers.

Without conscious volition her hands raised to slowly undo the buttons of his shirt. A sigh of relief escaped her when they encountered the smooth hardness of his shoulders and chest before sliding down to become lost in the dark tangle of matted hair, his heartbeat accelerating until it matched the uneven beat of her own.

"Yes, honey . . . touch me. I want to feel your hands on my body. God, yes. . . ." As he muttered the words against her neck, his mouth began a slow, tantalizing exploration of its own.

"David, David," she sobbed, her voice hoarse with emotion.

Suddenly his movements became almost frantic, his hands nearly tearing at her clothes in his urgency. After dispensing of them he stood up, shrugging his unbuttoned shirt aside while his eyes burned hotly into hers. A jolt of almost unbearable desire pierced her as he ran his hand slowly down his own body, and she knew he was remembering her hands and how they had often performed the same movements for him.

Closing her eyes, she heard the sounds as he unbuckled his belt, and she didn't have to look to imagine the powerful, sensual thrust of his body.

"Look at me," he demanded, his warmth half over her as he lay beside her shaking form. Biting her lip, she shook her head negatively, gasping as his hand cupped her breast, his thumb sending waves of longing through her as it circled the hardening nipple. Eyes flying open in unwilling response, she felt completely vulnerable as she met his triumphant look.

As if to reward her for complying with his demand, his hands began a slow, sensual arousal of her warm flesh. Lips parted to draw breath through her aching lungs, Anna moistened their dryness with her tongue.

"Don't," he whispered. "Let me. . . ."

His tongue tracing the outline of her lips broke the last shred of control she possessed, and she clutched the back of his powerful neck frantically, trying to draw him into her mouth.

David resisted the clutching of her hands, and his own became still on her body. Bewildered, she looked up at him, and she became lost in the sensual world of his demand.

"That's right, honey. I want you to watch while I love you," he muttered, his hands once again moving against her. "Tell me what you want . . . tell me!"

"David, please . . ."

"I want you to say it, damn you," he groaned, lowering his head and capturing her nipple in his mouth, biting down briefly before releasing it, and ignoring her cry of pain.

More than physical pain pierced her heart as she gazed at him pleadingly. He was making her pay for ever rejecting him, wanting her to beg for the pleasure he could give her. If she complied, his revenge would be complete, she mourned, for he would take her pride as well as her body.

David was playing a waiting game, staring at her with the promise of sensual fulfillment in the slumbrousness of his green eyes. Suddenly nothing mattered but this moment . . . and nothing could prevent the words which poured from her mouth.

"I want you . . . please!"

"What do you want me to do," he murmured, tracing the contours of her cheekbones with a lazy finger.

"I . . . I want you to make love to me," she moaned, capturing his roving finger with her teeth. She felt more than heard his gasp at the contact, and as if something snapped inside of him, there were no more words. His lips parted hers with savage intensity while his hands moved against her skin, leaving her shivering as they trailed fire over her willing flesh, leaving not an inch of her unexplored.

There was no gentleness in their lovemaking. The blazing urge that consumed them both was timeless . . . a need greater for having been denied. As his body joined hers, she closed her eyes, gasping her response against his mouth.

"God," he groaned, as her body arched against him. "You feel . . . so good . . . so good!"

His words spiraled her pleasure upward, ever upward, as she forced him to respond to the urgency of her movements. Once again his mouth captured hers, his tongue a welcome invader which she greeted with delight. Her moans mingled and became lost with his, and as her body peaked toward fulfillment, she began making low, kittenish sounds deep in her throat, filling the air and intensifying the completeness of his satisfaction.

On leaden legs Anna lifted the wet print from the last water wash, and with a tired sigh placed it with the others on the heated drum to dry, after carefully squeezing out the excess water on a steel plate. She watched dispassionately as the slowly moving belt carried it around the heated drum before dropping it, dry, into the receiving basket.

Usually this was the most exciting part of her job—seeing the finished proof of her labor—but in this case she

144

had barely been able to make herself look at them. Averting her eyes from the basket, Anna walked over to the sink, washing her hands thoroughly to remove the last traces of developing fluid from her skin. The eerie light intensified her pallor, and she stared at the thinness of her wrists with horror.

What in the world was she doing to herself? She was letting her despondency make a skeleton out of her, giving in to the misery that was eating at her soul. She had to start living again . . . she had to fight back!

Removing her apron with shaking fingers, she quickly gathered together the finished prints, hurrying her steps. She needed to get out of this closed-in space, this eerie nether world, and return to the light, where she wouldn't have to be alone with the memories tormenting her.

It was late by the time she had catalogued the last print and with a tired groan placed the last batch between its protective cardboard covers. Slipping it into the box with the others, she hurriedly placed the lid over the top, feeling sick with relief as the last reminder was out of sight.

With her head in her hands Anna stared at the white box in the mailing tray, neatly labelled and ready to go when Carla returned in the morning. If only her own life could be catalogued so neatly, she thought with a sigh. Pressing her fingers against her eyes, she tried to ignore the pain slicing through her temples, but the headaches were becoming worse as the days passed.

Her inability to eat had a great deal to do with the pain, but even this knowledge couldn't stem the churning of her stomach. It was as if her body were tuned to self-destruct, she thought fancifully, but her smile had no amusement behind it.

How long had she been like this, she wondered. A month? Yes . . . it was just over a month since she and Carla had come home. A month of burying herself in work until she was tired enough to sleep at night . . . and too busy to think during the day.

Many times she had wished away that week in Long Beach, for the results for her had been disastrous. Walking to the door with her coat over her arm, Anna looked at the clock over Carla's desk. It was well past midnight, and she ached in every muscle of her body. Locking the door to the studio securely behind her, she stood for a moment under the eave of the building before turning the collar of her coat up as a protection against the pouring rain. Her body locked tightly within its cloak of numbing tiredness, Anna walked the short distance to her car, barely aware of the moisture spraying her face and running in rivulets down her exposed neck. It seemed she had lost the ability to feel much of anything, and with a twisting anguish deep within her she prayed that soon she would also be incapable of remembering.

Driving the distance to her apartment automatically, Anna wondered when she had stopped thinking of it as home. Home was where the heart was, she thought morosely, and she felt as if for the second time in her life hers had been torn from her body. Parking the car, Anna turned off the ignition, leaning her forehead momentarily against her hands, which clutched the steering wheel as if for support. Just a short distance from the car to her rooms, but the effort seemed to be almost more than she could dredge from within. Sleep . . . how sensuous a word it was when coupled with the exhausting tiredness of mind and body. One could escape if there were no dreams . . . at least for a few hours. This thought and this thought alone gave Anna the impetus she needed, and with a characteristic determination she forced her body from the car.

The next morning, eyes dulled with sleeplessness, Anna stood on the patio, shivering in the damp air. The morning was dingy and bleak, but at least the interminable rain had stopped in the night. Closing her eyes and wrapping her housecoat more securely around her, she let the icy wind whip at her trembling body voraciously, the discomfort almost a relief after the long torturous hours she had just spent in the prison of her room.

The musty smell of damp concrete rose to engulf her senses, mingling in her mind with the unwelcome memory of salt, surf, and sunshine. Even her favorite retreat was denied her now, for she would see David's eyes in the sparkle of sunlight on ocean . . . hear his voice in the echo of wind whistling through the cliffs.

David . . . her mind whispered insidiously. A vivid picture of his golden-brown body sprawled indolently between white sheets, his chest rising and falling evenly in satiated sleep, came to her mind. He had seemed so beautiful lying there, his thick black lashes fanning his cheeks, and she remembered feeling an almost irresistible urge to stay snug within the shelter of his arm, which had been draped carelessly across her own body.

Of course, she had fought the urge, slipping from the bed and donning her clothes like a thief in the night . . . and like a thief, slipping into the hotel room she shared with Carla with noiseless tread. That had been the sensible thing to do . . . But God! Why had she denied herself a few more hours in his arms?

The next morning they had met for breakfast, and she had been shocked at how easy it had been for David to pretend nothing had happened between them. She had looked in vain for a new tenderness in his expression, a caring in his manner toward her, and instead been devastated by his remoteness. Within her subconscious mind she must have expected the giving of her body to act as a catalyst, changing forever his resentment and turning it into the love she sought so desperately.

The dream was far from the reality, she thought cynically. The rest of that day was lost in a gray haze of misery, but she must have been a better actress than she'd ever imagined, for Carla and Carl didn't seem to suspect anything was wrong, even on the close confines of David's boat during their return to Long Beach.

The rest of the convention passed in a blur of activity, for already she had begun using work as a panacea. Of David she saw little, and then only from a distance. It seemed as if now, after having succeeded in his purpose, he no longer felt any desire to single her out. Even his goodbye had been said formally in the lobby of the *Queen Mary,* with Carl and Carla included. Maybe his eyes had lingered on her for a moment longer than necessary, but his jaw had clenched, and without anything personal being said he had turned and walked away.

At that moment the small part of her which had kept hope alive throughout the long years without David finally withered and died . . . and she knew that for her there could be no more hope. The misunderstandings would remain forever unspoken and unresolved, and as she watched his tall lithe body stride away from her, she fought the inner voice urging her to call his name. Because of the omission the girl she used to be tormented her, and she woke up in sweating agony throughout the night . . . piteously calling his name.

For what seemed the hundredth time that morning Anna looked up at the clock on the studio wall, her brow furrowed in worry. Carla still hadn't shown up for work, and it was nearly eleven o'clock. It just wasn't like Carla to be late, for she was always religiously at her desk at nine o'clock. On the few occasions she'd been delayed there had always been a phone call to defray any anxiety or inconvenience. *There must be something wrong,* Anna fretted, *or she would at least have phoned.* There had been no answer at Carla's, and Anna bit her lip with indecision. Should she check with the police?

Just as her hand clenched the receiver, Anna heard

the front door slam and the sound of Carla's brisk footsteps tapping across the floor of the reception lounge. Sagging with relief, Anna wiped her forehead with a shaking hand, fighting against tears of reaction.

Suddenly Carla burst into the room, and Anna felt anger replacing her earlier anxiety.

"What in hell do you mean, coming in this late," she stormed, clenching her fist in her lap.

With a look of almost comical surprise, Carla, stopped in the center of the room, her eyes widening as she took in at a glance Anna's distraught figure. For the first time Carla looked at Anna . . . really looked at her, and she was appalled by what she saw. She had been so wrapped up in her own affairs, she hadn't noticed the physical evidence of her friend's deterioration, and with a gasp she ran to her.

"Honey, are you all right?" she asked, frightened by the whiteness of Anna's face.

Anna seemed to hear Carla's voice from a great distance, and with a gasp she slipped from her chair to the floor.

"Al," Carla screamed in panic, kneeling beside Anna's prostrate body.

"What . . ." Al boomed, the sound of the door reverberating as it was thrust against the wall with force and Al surged into the room.

"I knew it!" Al grumbled, kneeling beside Anna and shaking his head. "I told her if she kept on killing herself with work, something like this would happen."

"For God's sake, get some water," Carla cried.

Handing her the water just moments later, Al stood silently staring down at the still form that lay defenseless as Carla tried forcing the water between lips which refused to open. "Is she going to be all right?"

"She's fainted," Carla mumbled, taking her handkerchief and wetting it. Wiping Anna's face, Carla looked up at Al. "Get your car and bring it around front, will you? We've got to get her to emergency."

By the time they reached the hospital Carla was nearly frantic. This was more than just a faint, she thought in despair. It was as if Anna's subconscious were resisting, fighting against waking up, and Carla felt fear slicing through her as she held Anna's head in her lap, cramped in the back seat of Al's Volkswagon.

Al carried Anna's inert form through the large double doors of the emergency entrance to the hospital, while Carla hurried along beside him. As soon as they reached the desk, the nurse on duty looked up impatiently. Eyes widening as she noted Anna's unconscious figure in Al's arms, she wasted no time in summoning two orderlies.

"God! I feel so helpless just sitting here," Carla moaned, twisting her hands in agitation.

"I know, but there's nothing more you can do, Carla. You gave them all the particulars for their records, including the impossibility of any kind of a drug overdose. That probably saved them some time."

"Then what's taking so long?"

Al turned his head to reply to Carla's question, but just at that moment she jumped up from the bench they were occupying and ran toward a white-coated figure emerging from Anna's room.

"Doctor . . . how is she?"

"Are you a relative?"

"The closest thing she's got to one," Carla retorted impatiently.

The doctor, seeing the deep concern written plainly upon Carla's distraught face, relented on hospital discipline. Smiling reassuringly, he said, "She'll be fine, don't worry. At a guess I'd say she's been pushing herself too hard and starving herself in the process. She's also in a highly nervous state, which could be a result of malnutrition, though

I doubt it. Do you know if Miss Mason has had any kind of traumatic experience, such as the loss of a loved one?"

"Not to my knowledge, doctor," Carla replied hesitantly. "She has no relatives as far as I'm aware."

"In that case I suppose we can rule out emotional stress, though all the indications point to that diagnosis.

"Can she come home?" Al asked, walking up behind Carla.

"I'm afraid not," he replied. "Miss Mason needs plenty of rest and proper nutrition. She lives alone, doesn't she?"

"Yes, but . . ."

The doctor interrupted Carla with a raised hand and a smile of apology. "I'm sorry, but I really feel it would be better for Miss Mason to spend a few days here where she'll be able to receive the proper care."

"She won't like that one little bit," interjected Al with a shake of his shaggy head.

"Can we see her, doctor?" Carla asked.

"Of course, but don't stay too long. I want her to get all the rest possible," he replied, before nodding and moving toward another room across the hall.

Anna looked so much like a wan little ghost lying within the pristine whiteness of the hospital bed that Carla couldn't control the tears which burned behind her eyelids. Taking a deep breath to control herself, she whispered, "Hello, honey. You sure gave us a scare."

Anna smiled sleepily. "I'm sorry, I don't know what caused me to do a stupid thing like that."

"Overwork, that's what," Al muttered, himself moved by Anna's inert form.

"Don't say 'I told you so,' Al," she laughed. "You warned me, but I didn't listen, did I?"

"Women!" Al exclaimed in disgust. "When the time comes that one of you'll listen to a mere man, I'll have one foot on a banana peel and the other in the grave, and be deafened by the sound of old Gabriel's horn."

At his gentle teasing Anna smiled tiredly, fighting to keep her eyes open. The doctor had given her an injection to help her sleep, and she was beginning to feel its effects. She barely heard Al and Carla's murmured good-byes, sinking down pleasurably into a longed-for unconsciousness, and was already deeply asleep before they had even left the room.

The next three days went by swiftly, or so it seemed to Anna. In between sleeping she ate whatever she was given, at first fighting down nausea. At last, though, the enforced rest served its purpose, and she began eating with renewed appetite, anxious to gain her strength and her release from the hospital.

At last the day came for that release, and Anna waited anxiously for Doctor Miller to arrive and sign her out. Carla and Carl had already been to visit her and were waiting in the hall, ready to take her back to Carl's apartment. She had argued with Carla, insisting she was perfectly able to take care of herself, but Carla wasn't having any of that, at least for the next couple of days. Carl, possessing two bedrooms, was equally insistent, and Anna still didn't feel strong enough to fight both of them. Carla would be there during the day, and when she returned home to her children, Carl would take over. When the doctor had endorsed the plan as eminently suitable, Anna knew she had lost the battle, feeble though it had been.

"Doctor Miller," Anna gasped in surprise. "I've been waiting for you, and when you arrive, I don't even hear you come in," she laughed.

"How do you feel?"

"Wonderful," she grinned, looking at his gruff-seeming face confidently, knowing by now that it hid a gentle man.

"Anna, do you remember the afternoon you were admitted nearly a week ago," he asked, sitting beside her on the edge of the bed and taking hold of her wrist.

"Of course," she answered, staring at his bent head as he took her pulse.

"I suspected something during my examination of you, but it was a little too soon to tell," he murmured, raising his head to look at her but still keeping hold of her hand.

Anna's eyes widened apprehensively. "What is it? What's wrong with me?"

"Now, now. There's no reason to get upset," he soothed. "As long as you're not working yourself into the ground, you're extremely healthy, as I've told you before."

"Then what . . ."

"You're pregnant," he remarked bluntly, his eyes never leaving her face. He seemed to be waiting for signs of shock, despair even, and was somewhat relieved at the calm way Anna took the news.

"Are . . . are you sure?"

Nodding his head, the doctor took a deep breath, straightening his shoulders and finally releasing her hand. "This friend who has visited you, hmmm . . . is he . . .?"

"Carl? Oh, no! He's not the father," she muttered quickly.

"He seems fond of you, that's why I asked. Is there any chance of the father marrying you?"

Anna couldn't resent the doctor's probing into her personal life, for she knew that it was truly concern for her situation that prompted it. He was kind, and suddenly Anna felt the need to talk, to confide in someone she could trust. Taking a deep breath, Anna told him about her relationship with David from five years ago until the present.

As her words faltered into silence, the doctor ran a hand over the unruly thickness of his hair, his mouth pursed in concentration. "Either this fellow is a complete bounder or he cares more for you than he'll admit," he remarked earnestly. "I think you should tell him about the baby and give him a chance to show his true colors."

153

"I . . . I need time to think, Doctor Miller. I wouldn't want him if he were coming back to me only for the baby," she remarked firmly, her own determination hardening with the words.

"Well, as long as you want this child, then I guess you're capable of raising it on your own if the need arises. You do want the baby?"

"More than anything in the world," she breathed, a serene glow settling in her eyes as she thought of the child. "No one could want a baby more than I, doctor . . . no one!"

"In that case, I suggest you find the doctor of your choice to care for you during your pregnancy," he smiled. "I'll start you on prenatal vitamins, and he'll take it from there."

"Oh! But . . . couldn't you be my doctor?"

Nodding his head, he rose to his feet. "If you'd like me to care for you . . . I'll be more than happy to oblige. I have private offices not far from here, and I'll be relieved to be able to keep my eye on you and keep you from neglecting yourself," he laughed, his eyes twinkling.

"Believe me," she breathed fervently. "I won't do anything to risk the baby's health in any way."

"Since you've been one of my better patients, I must say I believe you. Here's my business card. Call tomorrow and arrange your next appointment with my receptionist. I'll want to see you in two weeks . . . no longer," he warned, walking across the bare confines of the hospital room and opening the door. "Get those vitamins before you leave and make sure you've gained some weight before I see you again," he growled, shaking an admonishing finger at her before quietly closing the door behind his portly frame.

CHAPTER NINE

"Carla," Anna squealed in delight. "Let me see it!"

Glowing with an inner radiance, Carla extended her left hand toward Anna, immensely proud of the shimmering diamond adorning the third finger.

"I'm so very happy for you both," Anna choked, her eyes filling with emotional tears. "You're just right for each other . . . I don't know why I never noticed it before."

"Probably because I was such a beast to him," Carla laughed.

"You were, rather," Anna grinned. "I hope he knows what he's letting himself in for!"

"He does . . . he does," Carla crowed in triumph. "The miracle is . . . he loves me anyway." Carla's eyes softened, bringing another lump to Anna's throat as she watched her friend absent-mindedly turn the ring on her finger.

Anna had spent the three days since leaving the hospital being coddled and loving every minute of it. Sensing their need to be alone, she had gone to bed much earlier than she'd felt the need to, but the rest had done her the world of good. She felt completely well again, and even the slights bouts of morning sickness only made her delirious with joy. The only cloud on her horizon was the worry over whether or not to tell David, but slowly she was coming to the realization that he had the right to know no matter what he decided to do. She'd have his child to love, and her own happiness was intensifying with every day that passed.

"Listen, Anna," Carla remarked worriedly, interrupting the flow of Anna's thoughts. "I'm worried about you staying alone tonight. Are you sure you don't want me to collect the kids and come back here for the night?"

"Don't be silly. Carl had a late appointment this evening, but he should be back by ten o'clock at the latest," Anna reassured. "I haven't had a fainting spell since that last one in the hospital, and I'm perfectly able to care for myself. Speaking of the kids, what do they think of you remarrying?"

Anna hoped her attempt at changing the subject would work, and to her relief Carla began enthusing about Carl's relationship with her children. Apparently they all got along beautifully, much to Carla's satisfaction.

With several motherly instructions to Anna concerning her welfare, Carla left for home, and Anna breathed a sigh of relief. Running water in the bathtub, Anna sprinkled bath crystals in freely, wrinkling her nose pleasurably as the fragrant steam rose to her nostrils. She had showered and washed her hair this morning, but she felt the need to be indolent . . . and a bath was just the thing.

Lying back with a sigh, her hand automatically reached out to caress her stomach, and she laughed aloud at her nonsensical searching. There wasn't the slightest swelling to indicate the baby was nestled securely within her body . . . and wouldn't be for awhile yet!

Drowsily content, Anna soaked until the water cooled and the skin of her hands became wrinkled like a prune.

The bath had made her sleepy, and with a yawn she left the tub, drying herself on a large, fluffy bath towel until her skin glowed. Wrapping the towel around her, she made for the bedroom. She'd just turn out the lights after getting her nightgown on . . . and climb between the sheets, she decided with a smile of anticipation.

The strident ringing of the doorbell startled her out of her somnolent state, and she frowned in surprise. Hurriedly slipping her robe over her nightgown, she went to the door. Had Carl forgotten his key?

"David," she gasped, her eyes widening in shock as she stared at the indolently lounging figure in the corridor.

"Aren't you going to ask me inside, Ann?"

Without waiting for her reply David moved past her, looking about him at the luxury of Carl's sumptuously decorated living room, a mocking smile crossing the harsh severity of his face.

Raising a shaking hand to brush at a stray curl made unruly by the steam of the bath, Anna took a shuddering breath, finally managing to tear her eyes away from David's overpowering presence. Closing the door nervously, she followed him into the living room before moving toward the bar, its black and gold fitments giving her a barrier she needed when facing him.

"Would you like a drink, David?"

Lithe strides ate up the distance between them until David stood just in front of her, only the width of the bar between them. For the first time Anna looked at him fully, gasping at the harshly implacable look on his face.

"I didn't come for a drink," he growled insolently, his eyes raking her nightclothes meaningfully.

"H . . . How did you find me," she asked, clenching her hands at her sides defensively.

"Believe it or not, I called and spoke to Al, explaining that I was a friend of yours. He didn't want to tell me the

157

address, until I mentioned the Long Beach convention and told him I needed to speak to you urgently."

"You can't blame Al for that," she murmured. "He was only trying to protect me."

"Just how many men feel the need to . . . protect you, Ann?"

"What's that supposed to mean, David?" she retorted, lifting her chin defiantly.

"You know damn well what it means, you cheating little . . ."

"I don't have to stand here and take any abuse from you, David," she whispered, her face whitening from the savageness of his glare. Moving from behind the bar, she went to walk past him, only to be caught up short by his hand on her arm.

She would have bruises to show tomorrow, she thought, wincing from the pain of his fingers digging into her flesh . . . but the real damage would be on the inside and hidden from his gaze.

"Let me go," she demanded, attempting to twist out of his grasp. "You couldn't have cared less about me or it wouldn't have taken you nearly six weeks to find me. Why the urgency now, David?" she mocked.

"I've been up at convention headquarters attempting to tie up the loose ends of the Long Beach stint," he muttered, his mouth compressing angrily.

"Is that what you're doing now, David? Tying up a loose end?"

With a muffled oath he jerked her against the hardness of his body, his hand tangling in the back of her robe before moving up to clutch her neck. Hands pinned at her sides, she was unprepared for the savage assault of his mouth. As the angry pressure increased, she forced her mouth closed until her teeth tore at the inner flesh painfully, and she was forced to part her lips.

As if her compliance pleased him, his mouth went from

brutal to coaxing, and a whimper escaped her as once again she found herself responding to his mastery over her with blind passion. His lips moved with sure expertise over the curve of her chin until they nestled in the hollows of her throat.

"Where's the bedroom, honey?" David whispered, raising his head and looking commandingly into her eyes.

"No, David! I . . ." she began weakly, her words fading as the brilliant passion in his eyes defeated her.

As if sensing her acquiesence, David gathered her up in his arms, walking out of the room and into the hall, opening doors until he came to the one she was using.

Laying her down on the unmade bed, he moved away from her, and she stared up at his figure as it towered over her, puzzlement in her eyes. Slowly he began removing the tan jacket of the leisure suit he was wearing, revealing the silkiness of the chocolate-brown shirt underneath.

"The light," she murmured, a flush rising in her cheeks at the almost calculated abruptness of his movements.

"You've seen it all before, honey," he mocked, beginning to unbuckle his belt, the shirt having already joined his jacket draped carelessly over the chair by the side of the bed.

Anna closed her eyes, waiting for him to join her with a longing so intense, she felt like gasping out her agony. All she could think of at this moment was him . . . and the inescapable fact that he'd come for her after all. The bed depressed with his weight, and Anna gave herself up to his arms, feeling a shivering response as his hard hands deprived her of her nightgown and robe and moved surely over her body.

"David . . . David," she moaned, her hands clutching at the smoothly muscled hardness of his back as if she would never let him go.

"When will Carl be back?" David asked, lifting his

mouth from her breast and nodding toward the matching twin bed.

"Around ten," she murmured, until the full significance of his question smote her and she stiffened in his arms.

Dear God! It sounded as if he believed she and Carl shared this bedroom! Pushing at his shoulders wildly, she turned her head to avoid his descending mouth. He was here not out of a need to be with her, but to make her feel the tramp he thought her.

The contempt he felt was written plainly upon his face as he jerked her mouth around to meet his. There was cruelty there, too . . . and her heart ached for the tenderness she knew he was capable of. With a gasp she remembered the baby! She couldn't let him go on trying to force her response or she might lose the life she carried. She'd rather die under the sting of his contempt than lose their child.

Winding her arms around his neck, she looked into his eyes, caressing the hair at the back of his head. "David, be gentle . . . please," she breathed, her eyes pleading with him.

For timeless seconds their glances were locked together, hers begging him for understanding and his indecisive.

His basic decency, which had been buried beneath the force of his anger, came to the fore, and he closed his eyes remorsefully, moving away from her and sitting on the side of the bed. His elbows resting on his knees, he leaned his face against his hands.

She could hardly stand seeing his dejection. Leaning up on one elbow, she tentatively reached out and placed one small hand against the warmth of his back.

"David, I . . ."

"Don't touch me, for God's sake," he groaned, and she jerked her hand away as if burned. "Don't you realize I almost raped you?"

"You didn't mean it," she argued, irrationally defending the man she loved . . . even against himself.

"That's just it, Ann," he muttered, jumping up from the bed and once again donning his clothes. "I did mean it!"

Anna watched him dress, her own misery beyond words. Buttoning his shirt with fingers which visibly shook, he turned to her, and she quickly pulled the bedclothes tightly around her body.

"David, it's not what you think," she moaned, tears beginning to fall from her eyes. "I've been ill, and Carl . . ."

"Don't lie to me, Ann," he snarled, clenching his hands in the pockets of his slacks. "I came to find you because, God help me, I couldn't stay away."

"Oh, David . . ." she cried, her face losing its haunted expression momentarily.

"Let me finish," he ordered, removing one hand to rake his hair back from his forehead. As if he couldn't stand looking at her, he moved toward the window, keeping his back turned. "For five years I've fought against my memory of you and how good it was between us. Once I returned, I couldn't escape you anymore, Ann. Everywhere I turned your ghost was there, taunting me. I had to prove to myself that the reality would be disappointing, even if I hurt you in the process. For what it's worth, Ann . . . you've had your revenge."

"I never wanted revenge, David," she cried, fighting the sobs that were tearing at her chest.

"Didn't you," he murmured, his voice sounding sick with self-loathing. "Even there you defeated me, for when I called the studio this afternoon and realized from the address that you were living with Carl, all I could think of was revenge."

Moistening her lips with the tip of her tongue, she asked, "David, did you ever love me?"

Silence stretched into the room like a tangible force, and Anna held her breath, waiting for the answer.

"Loved, hated . . . what in hell does it matter now?"

"It matters to me," she whispered.

Taking a deep breath, he turned to face her, leaning back against the window. "After what I almost did to you tonight, I guess you've earned your pound of flesh, Ann. Yes, I loved you."

"Then why did you leave me the way you did?" Anna asked, her body tense as she waited for his answer.

"I couldn't stand being away from you, so I returned early from the expedition. When I couldn't find you, I went to our neighbor, Mrs. Parker, who told me you were in the hospital. I guess she thought I was crazy, running off like I did, only waiting long enough to hear the name of the hospital. Anyway, when I arrived I went up to the desk to find out what room you were in. The nurse on duty was speaking to the doctor, and when I heard your name mentioned, I . . ."

David's voice faltered and died, and Anna knew his thoughts were far away in the past. Suddenly his body tensed, and she saw a naked agony in his face . . . and she was afraid to hear his next words . . . but knew she must if she were to ever know the truth.

"They mentioned abortion," he snarled, closing his eyes against his grief. "The nurse was shaking her head, saying it was such a pity . . . a little girl. That's what made it worse," he groaned. "Knowing it was a baby girl . . ."

"Oh, David. If only you'd waited to talk to me . . . I could have explained everything."

"I walked out of there like a blind man. Talk to you? I couldn't stand the thought of ever seeing you again. I knew your career was important to you, Ann, but I never realized you'd destroy my child to achieve it. Did you know about the baby before I left . . . was that why you encouraged me to go on that expedition?"

"David, I wrote telling you about the baby, I swear it," she choked, realizing too late that he must have left before it could reach him.

"Do you think that makes it any better, Ann?" David

yelled, his voice alive with anger. "Do you think I would have agreed to an abortion just because you weren't ready to be burdened with my child? God, you make me sick to my soul," he snarled, striding toward the door. "For what it's worth, Carl's welcome to you. Have you told him you don't want any children, or doesn't it matter to him?"

"But I do want children," she cried, beginning to reach for her robe, ignoring the contemptuous way his eyes raked her body.

"Now that you've got your career firmly established at the expense of our child's life . . . now you're ready to play the little mother, is that it?"

"Will you let me explain?" Anna cried, following him into the living room.

"All I want at the moment is to get as far away from you as I can, Ann. I only hope you don't tear Carl's guts from his body, the way you did mine. Have Carl's child, Ann. I'm beyond caring now," he muttered, opening the door and staring at her shivering body, which appeared to be rooted to the center of the floor. "But I hope it's a little girl, so that every time you look at her, you remember that other baby you didn't have the time for!"

The slamming of the door reverberated in her ears, and with a cry of anguish Anna threw herself down on the couch, uncaring if her tears stained the brocaded surface. She knew she'd never see David again. Remembering how impossible he had made it for her to contact him before . . . it would be even more so now that his hate and bitterness toward her was finally out in the open.

As if from a great distance, Anna could hear the sobbing moans she was making in the quickly darkening room, the depth of her grief almost frenzied in its intensity. It was as if all the hurt and despair of the past and present were merging, wracking her body with insidious tendrils of desperation.

"Anna, for God's sake, what's wrong?"

So wrapped up in her own misery, Anna hadn't been aware of the sound of Carl's key in the lock. In fact her preoccupation was so great that it wasn't until he was kneeling beside her that her muddled brain registered another presence in the room at all.

"I'm calling the doctor," he cried, jumping to his feet and striding toward the telephone.

"Carl . . . don't," she moaned, and momentarily he slowed his stride, turning to face her indecisively.

With tremendous effort Anna pulled herself upright, wrapping her arms around her body, which shook uncontrollably.

With a muffled oath Carl strode into his bedroom, returning quickly with his own warm terrycloth robe, which he placed tenderly around her shoulders before sitting beside her.

His kind concern was too much, and with a muffled cry Anna threw herself against the solid warmth of his body, and his arms circled her comfortingly, one large hand patting her back with endearingly clumsy movements.

"What's happened to make you like this, Anna?"

"Oh, Carl," she sobbed, her small slender fingers clutching the front of his shirt as if afraid to let go.

With muffled incoherence Anna began talking, and Carl had to bend his head to make any sense at all of her explanation. Almost imperceptibly, though, her voice lost much of its passionate involvement, and by the time she finished, there was a dead and hopeless quality to her words which in itself frightened Carl.

For awhile there was silence in the room. Exhausted with grief, Anna rested quietly against Carl until with a feeling of reluctance she pulled herself out of his arms.

"I could kill him for this," Carl said quietly, as if he were remarking upon the weather. Raising her eyes to his face, Anna gasped at the harshness of his expression. His words had been spoken so dispassionately that she couldn't help gasping at the obvious sincerity in Carl's manner. Carl had always seemed so calm and placid, and Anna couldn't help being appalled by this change in him.

"Carl, you don't understand!"

"What don't I understand? He thought the worst of you staying in my apartment . . . that I do understand. What I can't forgive is his coming here with the express intention of physically abusing you. The man must be mad!"

"If he is, then it's all my fault," she moaned, staring in front of her with sightless eyes, and biting down viciously on her lower lip to control its trembling.

Carl's body jerked violently as he turned to her. "How can you say that, Anna? If he chose to think the things he did without even giving you a chance to explain, then I'd say he was the one who needs the guilt feelings, not you!"

How could she expect Carl to understand, when he didn't know all of the bizarre misunderstandings which had warped David's love and trust in the past? Carl was right in thinking she shouldn't blame herself, for fate had taken the love she and David shared and distorted it with a lavishly cruel hand. David had reacted, as she had, through the depths of feelings which had made them irrational and unable to control the situations they found themselves in.

"I'm going to fix you a brandy, and I expect you to drink every drop," Carl remarked, rising to his feet and walking toward the bar.

"Yes, sir!" Anna quipped, her rather shaky laughter bringing an answering smile to Carl's face.

Watching him as he prepared their drinks, Anna knew that she'd have to confide in Carl, if only to prevent any more misunderstandings. From the look on his face Carl was feeling pretty rotten . . . and not just for her sake, she realized. He had liked David and now felt betrayed, as if his own character judgment had been at fault, and she couldn't sit by and let those feelings fester into real hatred.

She wouldn't put it past Carl to seek David out, for he was old-fashioned and might form the quixotic notion of defending her honor. The thought brought a smile to her face, a smile which swiftly faltered as she thought of the shame she would feel if such an eventuality ever materialized. She could just imagine what David would think!

"Thank you," she smiled, taking the drink from Carl and patting the couch. "Get comfortable, Carl, and I'll do my best to shed some light on this mess for you, but only if you'll make me a promise."

"What will I have to swear to?"

"Not very much," she smiled, taking another sip of the cool liquid in her glass and enjoying the normalcy of the sound of ice clinking on the sides. "I want you to promise me you'll never make any attempt to contact David or to repeat to him any of what I'm going to tell you."

"Hmmph! That'll be an easy promise to keep," he retorted grimly.

"Then I have your word?" Anna's question was eager, and she waited for Carl's confirmation with bated breath.

"You have my word," he replied quietly.

During the next hour Carl was careful never to interrupt her, sensing her need to talk unrestrainedly. Only once during her narration did he muffle an oath, quickly apologizing before getting up and striding up and down the carpet.

When her story finally drew to a close, Anna raised her eyes from the torturous twisting of her hands in her lap. "Now can you understand why David wasn't to blame, Carl?"

Carl's pacing stopped, and he turned to lean against the bar. With lowered head he pondered Anna's question before raising pitying eyes to hers. He knew from things he'd observed that David was impetuous, and the poor bastard had paid in blood for his impetuosity. From what he could make out, their love for each other had been so strong

166

that neither of them had been able to trust in its beauty and ability to last. He winced inwardly for the anguish Anna had suffered, but being a man himself, could understand the terrible anger David must have felt thinking his child had deliberately been destroyed.

"I think I can understand now, Anna," he remarked with a sad quirk to his lips. "It was rather like a train wreck where one car collides and all the others pile up behind. Don't you think it's about time one of you began clearing the track, honey?"

"What do you mean?"

"You love him, good or bad, right or wrong. Am I right?"

Anna nodded, lowering her head to avoid Carl's demanding expression.

"A love like that is rare, Anna. Don't you think you owe it to both David and yourself to make one more attempt at reaching him?"

Jumping up from the couch, Anna walked toward the picture window, absently studying the panoramic view of the San Francisco skyline, lit up and shining and showing no evidence of the ordinary grime of life which she knew was beneath the surface. If the lights suddenly went out, there would be only darkness, with scurrying shapes desperately trying to avoid any dangerous obstacles. That's the way her relationship with David had always been, she realized with surprise. Neither of them had been equipped for the pitfalls when the light finally faded . . . and neither of them had trusted each other enough to bridge the gap, which was now a chasm.

Should she do as Carl suggested and make one last attempt to reach David? She needed him so much, and . . . The burgeoning excitement inside Anna quivered and dispersed, leaving an aching throb in its place.

"I can't, Carl," she whispered despairingly. "He'd never believe me."

"I think he would, and the hospital records of the accident would back you up—not that he'd need any proof," he reiterated quickly.

"Carl, I'm going to have his baby," she said quietly, watching his face for his reactions. "Don't you understand? How many evenings have we spent together here or in my apartment, Carl? Even Carla had to be reassured before she would believe she wasn't coming between you and me. David might eventually believe the truth about the past, but it would be asking a lot of him to believe we've never had a sexual relationship. If you were in his place, could you be entirely certain the child was yours?"

Carl looked at Anna with appalled eyes. "Anna, you've at least got to give him that chance!"

"Even if I could convince him the child was his, do you think I'd want him under those circumstances?"

"But . . ."

"No, Carl," she retorted, raising her chin in a pathetic gesture of pride. "I . . . I just can't take anymore. I'm leaving here tomorrow, and I think the best thing to do under the circumstances is to get away for awhile, somewhere I can rest and think about the future. I'll talk to Al in the morning, but right now I feel drained. Please don't talk any more about it!"

"You're right, darling," he muttered, suddenly contrite. "You're ready to drop, and here I am badgering you. What a clumsy oaf I am!"

Smiling with effort, Anna walked toward the bedroom door. With her hand on the knob she turned, her eyes locking with his. "You're my dear, dear friend, and I thank God for that," she said, the softness of her voice lending emphasis to her words, causing a dull flush to stain Carl's cheeks in embarrassment. "Please stay my friend and keep your promise, Carl."

168

CHAPTER TEN

With Anna's final plea ringing in his ears Carl stood staring at the closed bedroom door, a grimly set look to his mouth. After endless minutes his tense body sagged defeatedly, and he raked a shaking hand through his hair.

Removing his gray suit coat he dropped it carelessly over the silver brocade couch, staring down at the contrasting colors absentmindedly. With a strangled oath he raised his hand to his throat, removing his tie with savage movements and flinging it across the room in disgust.

What in the world had possessed him to make such a promise? A friend was supposed to be there to help, but Anna had tied his hands good and proper, he mused angrily. Between the two of them she and David had messed up their lives together once, and he couldn't see any way to avoid them doing so again. God! What a mess!

Turning to the bar, Carl poured himself a stiff measure of Scotch, wincing as the first swallow burned its way past his constricted throat. His only intention to get good and drunk, Carl once more raised the glass to his lips, stopping suddenly as an idea crossed his mind. Placing the glass back onto the bar with such force that half the liquid sloshed out of it, he chuckled out loud.

Ordinarily such a waste of his best Scotch would have made his thrifty soul shudder in protest, but at the moment he was too elated to care. Walking to the phone, he picked up the receiver, cradling it in his hands while he swiftly dialed the number with shaking fingers.

A voice husky with sleep answered, and a tender smile curved Carl's mouth. So his love was grouchy when she first woke up, was she? He'd just have to think of a less alarming way of waking her then, he promised himself, feeling his breath quicken at the thought.

"Darling, it's Carl," he said, the huskiness of his voice shaking slightly at the intensity of his thoughts.

"Since I don't know any other man who'd call me at this hour, let alone refer to me as darling, I guessed it was you," Carla muttered with a valiant attempt at shaking the last tendrils of sleep from her mind.

"There had better not be any other man," he retorted with a laugh. "Listen, honey. I have to talk to you. Can I come over?"

"Carl, is something wrong?" Carla asked anxiously. "You sound . . . strained."

"Don't worry, it's nothing you can't handle."

"Carl, if you're planning to . . . to . . ." she spluttered, the words tumbling over themselves in her haste. "You know the kids . . ."

His muffled laughter effectively drowned out the rest of her sentence, and he had to fight to gain control of his mirth, almost losing the battle. He could almost feel her seething silence, he thought delightedly.

"Honey, though the idea certainly appeals, it's Anna I want to talk about," he explained, his voice becoming grim.

"Carl," she demanded. "She's all right, isn't she? Nothing's happened? Oh, God! I knew I shouldn't have left her until you got home!"

"It's nothing like that, darling," he reassured. "I'll ex-

170

plain everything when I get there. Put some coffee on, okay? I think we're going to need it!"

Later, sitting in the coziness of Carla's breakfast nook, Carl's voice finally faltered to a stop. Head bent, he noticed with a sense of surprise that his coffee had grown cold, as he absentmindedly fingered the brown earthenware mug between his hands.

A muffled sob penetrated his absorption, and with a jerk his head lifted in surprise.

"The poor little thing," Carla murmured, tears unashamedly making rivulets down her pale cheeks. "To have to face losing her baby alone with no one to turn to. Even if he knew the truth about the accident, how could he ever make up to her for the way he ran out on her when she needed him so desperately?"

"As far as losing the baby, I think he's already begun making that up to her," Carl remarked drily.

"How can you say that," she retorted, her voice shocked by the apparent callousness in the voice of the man she was planning to marry. "Nothing can make up for the loss of a baby . . . nothing!"

"Nothing except having another baby," he remarked, looking at Carla intently.

"Not even that . . ." she began, faltering to a stop as the meaning of Carl's words penetrated her consciousness. "You mean she's . . . she's . . ."

At Carl's affirming nod Carla seemed to crumple, a shaking hand coming up to rub at her temple. With jerky movements she rose to her feet, clasping Carl's coffee mug and gathering it together with hers. She didn't say a word as she moved through to the kitchen, and Carl also remained silent, knowing she needed time to adjust to the shock he'd just meted out to her.

He heard the sound of the faucet running as Carla obviously emptied the cold contents of their mugs down the sink, and as the sound subsided, he straightened in his seat

171

in anticipation of her return. He didn't have long to wait, for almost immediately Carla was standing in front of him, the aroma of fresh coffee filling the air.

"What are we going to do, Carl?"

"You mean what are you going to do, don't you?"

"Wait just a minute," she exclaimed, her expression reproachful. "What we do, we'll do together, Carl. After all, when we're married we'll be as one, remember?"

"Mmm," he murmured suggestively. "That idea I like!"

At the look in his eyes Carla turned away, only to have Carl's hand reach out and clasp her wrist. Drawing her closer, he ignored her spluttering protests, settling her inexorably upon his lap.

Carla's halfhearted battle died as soon as their lips met, and what had begun as a teasing exploration quickly turned to passion. With one arm locking her tightly to him Carl's other hand gently parted the lapels of Carla's frilly brunch coat, his fingers beginning a sensuous exploration of the throbbing pulse in her neck.

"You guys better cool it," murmured an amused voice from the hallway. "Susan will be here pretty soon."

With a cry of mortification Carla tore herself away from Carl's restraining arms, attempting to stand upright, only to feel his hands at her waist resisting her efforts.

Glaring impotently into his amused eyes, she ran a smoothing hand over the tumbled disorder of her hair.

"Breakfast ready, Mom?"

At Gary's innocent-sounding question Carla raised her eyes to the clock above her head. "I had no idea it was so late," she gasped, firmly pushing Carl's hands away and getting to her feet. "It'll have to be cold cereal this morning, okay?"

"Sure, Mom," Gary replied, looking down at his mother from his lanky adolescent frame. "Don't sweat it, we'll live!"

"Gary, I wish you'd stop using that awful slang," Carla

reprimanded automatically, hurrying through the kitchen door with a feeling of reprieve.

Gary's dark eyes, so similar to his mother's, followed her departure before turning to Carl with a grin.

"Boy, I've never seen Mom that shook up," he exclaimed wickedly. "She acted like I'd never caught you guys kissing before."

Carl laughed softly, watching with an unfamiliar sense of pride as Gary sat down across from him.

"Yes," he murmured, taking a swallow of coffee. "But that's the first time you've caught her kissing me back. Anyway, she's afraid you might have gotten the wrong impression."

"I know Mom better than that," he exclaimed earnestly. "You, too," he added belatedly.

"Thank you, son."

"What for?"

"For accepting me, and making it easy for your mother," he murmured, meeting Gary's eyes, his own expression serious.

Gary flushed, mumbling, "Heck, it's about time there was someone to take care of her. Believe me, it'll be a load off of my mind."

Unsure of the relationship growing between them, both Carl and Gary were somewhat relieved when Susan entered the room.

"Carl," she squealed, brown hair bouncing on chubby shoulders as she hurried over to sit beside him. "Did you come to drive us to school?"

At that moment Carla returned, a box of cereal tucked under one arm, precariously balancing bowls and milk on the other.

"No, he did not," she answered for Carl. "Carl and I have important matters to discuss Susan, so hurry up and eat or you'll miss the bus."

"But I want the kids to see my new father," she wailed beseechingly.

At Susan's words Carl's arm reached out to enfold her in a quick hug. Raising his eyes to Carla's, he murmured, "It'll only take a minute, honey."

Seeing her daughter's hopeful face raised to hers, Carla relented with a smile. "All right, but don't think you're going to wrap Carl around your finger all the time, young lady," she warned. Giving Carl a tender glance, she could tell her warning was much too late. He was well and truly wrapped, she thought, amusement mingling with poignant relief in her breast.

After saying good-bye to Carl and her two talkative offspring at the door, Carla hurried through the living room to the bathroom. Taking a quick shower, she hurried through her dressing with uncharacteristic carelessness. Entering the living room still tucking a powder-blue shirtwaister snuggly into the waistband of her cream pleated skirt, she looked cool and capable and felt anything but. . . .

Taking the telephone down from the ledge dividing the breakfast nook from the kitchen, she placed it upon the cluttered surface of the table, deciding against taking the time to clear the breakfast things away.

By the time Carl had returned, he found Carla writing busily upon a notepad, her head leaning casually upon her hand. For a moment he paused, enjoying the sight of yellow and gold roses on the walls and the way the sun poured through the large bay window, dancing against the wallpaper until it cast flickering shadows upon the table. His breath caught in his throat as a single beam played over the sleek blackness of Carla's hair, still unbound around her shoulders, until the glorious waves appeared almost blue to his bemused eyes.

Swallowing with difficulty, Carl resisted the urge to coax Carla into the bedroom. Thank God they were getting

174

married next weekend, he thought, smiling inwardly. He doubted if he could last much longer, especially if she looked at him as she was doing, he mused, straightening from his brief kiss of greeting and seating himself a safe distance away, the width of the table between them.

"Carl, I've just spoken to David," she exclaimed, excitement mingling with smugness in her voice as she noticed Carl's expression, which varied from surprise to astounded admiration.

"How in the world did you manage it so quickly, darling?"

"Simple," Carla laughed. "I simply contacted Mr. Curtis and told him you wanted David as best man at our wedding."

"You little devil," Carl exclaimed, jumping to his feet and hugging her enthusiastically. "I can see I'll have to be on my toes if I hope to deal with you!"

Carla giggled, her whole face alight with love as she looked up at him. "Anyway," she began innocently, lowering her head and beginning to draw circles on the pad in front of her. "David is on his way over!"

Carl's body tensed as she dropped her bombshell, staring at her bent head in disbelief.

"Just like that . . . with no objections," he muttered, groping for a chair and sitting down heavily. "How?"

"The same way I got Mr. Curtis to give me his number, silly," Carla giggled. "I asked him to be best man at our wedding. You said he was under this misapprehension that you and Anna had a thing going, so I decided to kill two birds with one stone."

"Woman," he murmured admiringly, gazing into her eyes. "I'm a very lucky man!"

CHAPTER ELEVEN

Anna wrapped her windbreaker more securely around her shivering body, crossing her arms in front of herself for extra warmth. With a broken zipper, and reaching only to her hips, it wasn't altogether the most sensible garment she could have chosen to wear on such a damp and bitterly cold day, but she derived comfort from its shabby familiarity.

She certainly needed all the comfort she could get, she thought bitterly. Coming here to this lonely stretch of Monterey Bay, its towering cliffs and white sand stark and desolate against the angry gray sky, had been a mistake. As she admitted as much to herself, the too-ready tears began filling her eyes, slipping silently down her pale cheeks and intermingling with the fine mist already coating her skin.

A powerful gust of wind struck suddenly, whipping around the black and gray rocks which surrounded the small cove, making her shiveringly aware that as a shelter from the wind it left a lot to be desired. Adjusting the hood of her windbreaker more securely in place, Anna was grateful for the warm, if slightly worn fur, which caressed her cheeks.

With a sigh of defeat Anna turned and began retracing her steps along the path. Her clothes were uncomfortably damp from the deceptively gentle mist, and her woolen slacks felt clammy against her legs. If she stayed out much longer she'd end up with pneumonia, she mused wryly, and although she was beyond caring about herself, she had to think of the baby.

At the thought of the possible harm she might be causing the tiny life inside of her, Anna quickened her steps, hurrying the last few yards up the almost perpendicular path. The cold air sliced painfully through her lungs with every gasping breath she took, and as she traveled the now rocky terrain, she cursed herself for walking so far in such uncertain weather.

It was raining in earnest now, the drops sliding down her cheeks and soaking through to the cable-knit sweater she was wearing beneath her coat. With a sigh of relief she finally came to the road which wound peacefully in front of the tiny cabin she had rented for two weeks. The only other visible dwelling was a quaint general store which carried everything from chewing gum to bed linens. Checking for traffic automatically, she began crossing the roughly paved road, looking down ruefully at her tennis shoes, which were not only sopping wet but now muddy as well.

Anna's feet were dragging tiredly as she began climbing the weathered and peeling steps which led to the front entrance of the cabin. There was a driveway of sorts which meandered around back of the tiny dwelling, but as it was unpaved except for a gravel covering, Anna opted for the stairs.

Built in three tiers, the wooden stairs were worn smooth in places, and Anna clutched the rickety railing gratefully as she climbed, aware of the danger of falling as her wet shoes once again slipped on the smooth wood. Finally reaching the top, she leaned exhaustedly against the railing which surrounded the long porch, her eyes straying absent-mindedly toward the general store.

Her eyes passed over the sleek lines of the car parked in front of the dilapidated old building, and with a gasp of disbelief she shuddered. The car was the same make and model as David's, she reassured herself, but that didn't mean anything. After all, she'd only seen his car briefly and in the dark. There were thousands of cars like his, and it was probably totally different in color from the black beauty parked across the road.

Clamping her jaws tightly together, Anna tried to stop the shaking which had seized her. She had to learn to live with the shattering sense of loss she felt every time she thought of David. What a fool she was, she thought bitterly. How could she even begin to put David finally and irrevocably out of her life in the place where it all began, here among the sands and sea of Monterey Bay?

Anna's introspective recriminations were interrupted by sudden pain in her fingers, and with a sense of shock she released her hold on the splintered rail. She saw the grooves from her fingernails scored deeply into the wooden surface, her eyes closing painfully.

It was no use, she thought despairingly. Even against the blackness of her eyelids the gouges appeared, and she was unable to stop the flowing images they created in her brain. Once this cabin had been built with love, each nail used to secure the old railing placed with care and fore-thought. Where was he now, that builder who had attempted to endow his creation with beauty as well as durability?

In her own way, along with other uncaring souls who had sheltered here, she too had left a scar upon its surface, which was already left defenseless by the ravages of time and a callous indifference as to its well-being.

Anna threw her head back in a defiant gesture, opening

her eyes and staring at the eaves under which she sheltered. The old boards were warped from the ravages made by the elements, giving them a sadly pathetic appearance. Wrapping her arms defensively around her shaking body, she tried unsuccessfully to fight off the feeling of being trapped . . . threatened.

Although her thoughts were foolishly imaginative, Anna couldn't bring herself to laugh at her fancies. She couldn't help thinking that her own life was beginning to bear certain similarities to this defeated old structure. David had built love inside of her layer upon layer, its reality apparently unshakable. Now that he was gone would loneliness eventually force her to capitulate? Dear God! Would she too endure, desolate and unloved, until she finally was reduced to allowing poor imitations of love into her life, their passing leaving gouges in her soul?

With a muffled sob Anna turned, opening the front door with trembling fingers. She would leave now . . . tonight! Though barely five o'clock it would be dark in an hour, and she couldn't bear the thought of being here once the sun had set. It was probably her pregnancy causing her to react in this hysterical manner, but somehow that didn't seem to make much difference to her now.

Turning on the lights in an attempt to dispel the shadows of early evening, Anna gazed around her blindly. She couldn't see the quaint charm of faded wood nor the hominess of the overstuffed sofa and chair nestled close to the cavernous stone fireplace. Now it all represented a prison of loneliness, and the walls seemed to be closing in on her.

Her breath coming in shallow gasps, eyes dilated in terror, Anna felt despair grip her as her legs suddenly seemed to give way underneath her. There was a pounding in her ears, reverberating around the small room until she closed her eyes in defeat, unable to withstand the darkness she felt enfolding her.

"Anna . . . for God's sake, answer me!"

Anna felt the shadowy mists rising, dispelled by the only person in the world who could light the darkness for her. She felt herself being lifted in strong arms, burrowing against his warmth like a small child seeking comfort. She clutched his shoulders, sliding her arms around his neck in a desperate attempt to hold on to the reality of his presence. *God . . . please let him be here!*

Carrying her to the sofa, David bent to deposit her gently among the cushions. When Anna stubbornly refused to relinquish her hold, he was forced to sit beside her, and with a cry she molded her body to his, her mouth feverishly seeking the throbbing pulse in his throat.

With a groan David's hand clutched at her hair, forcing the hood to her windbreaker aside impatiently. Pulling at the silken strands softly, he forced her head back, his lips covering her willing mouth as if he were starved for the taste of her. With a shaking hand he pushed her coat apart, seeking the fullness of her breasts beneath the confining covering.

"My God," he muttered disbelievingly. "You're soaked to the skin!"

Still drowning in the sensations aroused by his mouth, not to mention the exhaustion she felt by the sudden release from her nameless terror, Anna made no protest as David pulled away from her. Resting her head lethargically against the back of the sofa, she watched with dazed eyes as David began building a fire, admiring the way his large hands lifted the heavy wood from the pile stacked beside the fireplace.

In a surprisingly short time the fire was blazing, and as Anna felt the warmth she sighed in relief, realizing at that moment how cold she was. She wanted to question David but was afraid to open her mouth, clenching her teeth to prevent them from chattering.

It was taking nearly all the strength she had to control

the shuddering spasms which were suddenly wracking her body. Her fright must have generated heat, forming a kind of protection against the chill she'd suffered earlier, she thought. Now that the fear was removed, she was once again conscious of the clammy coldness of her flesh. Either that, or David's appearance had sent her into shock, she thought wryly. The latter seemed more likely, for she couldn't seem to move at all . . . except for the involuntary shivering coursing through her.

"Stand up!"

At David's harshly spoken words Anna's eyes once more flew open in alarm. She must have dozed for a few seconds, for she couldn't remember David going into the bedroom. Surely she would have heard his footsteps against the hardwood floor? With puzzled eyes she noticed the blanket she had last seen folded against the foot of the bed. What was he doing with it in his hands? she mused wonderingly.

"Damn it, Ann," he cursed, his face tightening impatiently. "Do you want to die of pneumonia?"

Suddenly his question pierced through her fog of semiawareness, and Anna obeyed him instinctively, her pleading gaze locked within the green depths of his eyes.

"Would you care?"

Her words were little more than a whisper, but she knew from the stiffening of his body towering over her that he'd heard. For a brief moment Anna thought she saw a spasm of anguish cross his face before he began methodically removing every stitch of her clothing.

"Don't David," she muttered, her words muffled by the sweater he was pulling over her head.

"Stand still, damn you," he snarled, subduing her frantic struggles with effort. "You've got to get out of these wet things, Ann."

"No . . . I," she moaned, crossing her arms defensively over her naked breasts, only to release them in a futile attempt at preventing him from stripping off her slacks. She managed to clutch the waistband, but her efforts were completely wasted against David's grim-lipped determination.

With a final warning look in her direction David walked back toward the sofa, where the blanket lay in a muddled heap. All the fight drained out of her, Anna stood in front of the fire, curling her toes into the large white rug beneath her feet. Her arms hung limply at her sides, and for the life of her she didn't think she had the strength left to lift them.

As she watched apathetically, David turned, the blanket clenched in his hands. He took two steps toward her, only to stop as if rooted to the spot. With widening eyes Anna noticed the expression on his face change as he gazed at her, unaware of the firelight turning her skin to molten gold.

"God, you're lovely," he muttered, a flush darkening the hard angles of his face.

Her skin feeling scorched with more than the heat of the fire, Anna rushed forward, grasping the blanket angrily and enveloping herself in its welcome protection.

"Why have you come, David? I thought you wanted to get as far away from me as possible."

Anna heard the bitterness in her words with disbelief. God . . . she'd been longing for David . . . aching for him, and now all she could do was yell at him like a shrew.

"That was before I talked to Carl," he retorted grimly, his eyes suddenly flaming with anger. "Why in hell didn't you tell me the truth, Ann?"

At the mention of Carl's name Anna's face registered the shock she felt, the sense of betrayal. She would have trusted Carl with her life, she mourned, fighting against the tears burning her eyes. This last blow was almost more than she could take, she thought despairingly. Now she was truly alone, for now even the deep friendship she'd shared with Carl was to be denied her. Well, she was damned if she'd let David know how bitterly she was hurt. If all she was to have left to her was lonely pride . . . then at least she could keep that intact!

"You wouldn't let me tell you the truth," she retorted, anguish distorting her expression. "You judged me on circumstantial evidence, David, and didn't even allow me to speak in my own defense."

By this time any control Anna had over her emotions was lost, her words flowing from her mouth without conscious volition. For too long she'd bottled up her emotions, but now all the hurt and pain she'd suffered in the past erupted from her like bitter gall.

"How does it feel to be both judge and executioner, David? You walked into that hospital, and because you thought you overheard someone mention abortion, you had so little faith in the love I had for you, you were willing to believe it unquestioningly. The pathetic thing about the whole situation was me, David . . . because I lay there calling for you, needing you desperately to help me through the agony of losing our baby," she sobbed, turning abruptly away from him and gazing into the flames, her shoulders drooping defeatedly. "Now that you know the truth, did you think everything would be all right . . . that we could take up where we left off?" she questioned bitterly. "How soon would it be before you judged me guilty of something else, David? Faith can't be manufactured . . ." Her words trailed off in a whisper.

"Oh, my God, what have I done?"

At the sound of the anguished remorse in David's voice Anna whirled around, looking at his face for the first time since she'd started speaking.

"David," she whispered, appalled at the whiteness of his face, the shock in his eyes. "Carl told you the truth, that's why you came."

183

Raking his hand violently through his hair, David sat down abruptly, his head cradled in his hands, muffling his words. Anna strained to hear, taking unsteady steps toward his dejected figure.

"Carla called asking me to be best man at their wedding. Up until then I was convinced you were involved with Carl," he explained, his voice tired. "I realize now that although the thought of you in his bed had me eaten up with jealousy . . . still, I wanted to believe the worst, Ann. All those years thinking I hated you when deep down inside I had to fight myself to keep from crawling back."

Anna twisted her hands tightly around her scant covering, looking down at David's thick dark hair with hope burgeoning inside of her like a flower opening after a spring rain.

"Ann, you couldn't despise me more than I do myself," he whispered, his voice cracking with emotion.

"You didn't know about the baby until I told you, did you?"

Slowly Anna's hand moved, and as her fingers began stroking the thickness of his hair, David's body convulsed violently; with a muffled sob Anna threw herself beside him, cradling his head in her arms.

Anna held David, letting his grief and remorse wash away the bitterness of the past for both of them. She felt as if she were going backward in time, finally able to weep with David over the loss of their child.

Emotion spent, she and David sat by the dying fire, their tears drying on their cheeks. They had talked themselves out, saying all the things which should have been said years ago. Anna could look back now and blame herself, for she had been so unsure of her own ability to attract David that she'd unconsciously held back her innermost thoughts from him, thus leaving their relationship open to the seeds of doubt which had festered and finally borne fruit. What she had been too young to understand was that David was as unsure of her love for him as she was of his for her.

Suddenly David's body convulsed with laughter, and Anna raised sleepy eyes to smile up at him.

"What's the joke?"

"I just remembered . . . I was supposed to be on my way to Carla's. After she told me she and Carl wanted me for best man, she invited me over to discuss arrangements. Instead I went to the studio to have it out with you, only to be told you'd left for Monterey. Since the old cottage had been torn down, I had quite a search on my hands. All I had to go on was the hope that you'd stick to the general area where we first met. Thank God my hunch was correct," he breathed fervently.

"Yes," Anna smiled in contentment. "We have such a lot to be thankful for, darling."

Another laugh rumbled through David's body.

"I realize now they were planning a spot of matchmaking, and they're probably tearing their hair out, thinking their plot backfired."

"Serves them right," Anna retorted, snuggling closer within the secure warmth of David's arms. "I can't wait to see their expressions when they find out we've been married all along. I just hope Carla's not hurt by the fact that I didn't tell her the whole truth," she worried.

"I think she'll be so relieved that we've found each other, she probably won't care one way or the other," he consoled. "Woman, you do realize you're losing that damn blanket, don't you?"

"Hmmm," she murmured, letting it slip further.

"You have no business lying here and tempting a starving man," he growled, scooping her up in his arms and walking toward the bedroom.

"Why don't you do something about it, then," she retorted provocatively, looking into his eyes and catching her breath at the wealth of love and passion she could read in their depths.

With David beside her on the bed the shadows were no longer terrifying. The long darkness was over, the dawning of shared understanding and trust breaking like a new sunrise over their love for each other.

Anna felt she would wait for the dawn before telling David of the secret nestled quietly within her body, wanting to see the joy soar in his eyes as the first rays of a new day washed the world clean again, ready for a new beginning.

Now you can reserve June's
Candlelights
<u>before</u> they're published!

♥ You'll have copies set aside for *you*
the instant they come off press.
♥ You'll save yourself precious shopping
time by arranging for *home delivery*.
♥ You'll feel proud and efficient about
organizing a system that *guarantees* delivery.
♥ You'll avoid the disappointment of not
finding *every* title you want and need.